PRAISE FOR
What I Would Tell You

"Julie Keon has written the quintessential must-read guidebook for parents of children with disabilities. She mines her own complex care parenting experience to speak the unspeakable and reflect on the unthinkable. In doing so, Keon offers the reader a hand of friendship and compassion. Julie Keon is a professional Life-Cycle Celebrant - her daily bread is made mentoring people through marriage, birth and death. It's this career that helps the author present a clear-eyed view of tragedy and triumph, joy and despair. Her wise and companionable prose will help any parent of a child with disabilities to learn that by making peace with grief and uncertainty, there is ample room for joy and pride. This is a life-changing and life-affirming book for all parents of complex children as well as those who love and support them."

~ **Donna Thomson,** *mother, author of "The Four Walls of My Freedom: Lessons I've Learned from a Life of Caregiving."*

"The revised edition of *What I Would Tell You* does not disappoint. It is a must-read for all parents, caregivers, family members, doctors and therapists to any child that has a disability. I was reminded page after page that it's okay to feel fear and pain but also that there would be immense amounts of joy and hope. I was reminded that I need to take care of myself and my marriage so that I can be the best mom I can be for my son. Most importantly, I was so gracefully reminded to be more present, in the moment, and to savour every second I have with the most beautiful little boy. I am forever grateful for Julie's willingness to put herself out there, for sharing her words of wisdom, her heart and her love with those of us just starting this experience of parenting. I am a better mom and person because of it."

~ **Jen Cunningham,** *Mom to Chase*

"*What I Would Tell You* is a candid, riveting account of what happens when you're told your precious newborn will not do any of the things you anticipated. Julie leads you through what to expect: how you might feel, how others might react and most importantly, what you can do to thrive and find meaning. This book is packed with compassion, practical wisdom and life-affirming insights. It's a must-read for parents, family and friends. Anyone seeking courage and resilience in the face of catastrophic events will benefit from it. *What I Would Tell You* is an indispensable guide for doctors and nurses and any professional who works with children with medical fragility. It illuminates the kind of care that empowers and uplifts, and the kind of care that can break down and further traumatize.

~ **Louise Kinross,** *BLOOM Editor, Holland Bloorview Kids Rehabilitation Hospital*

"Julie's book is an essential guide for families with medically fragile children. It validates their experience, recognizes their resilience, helps break the silence and reduces the isolation that many families experience throughout this rewarding yet challenging journey. It is also a must-read for anyone working with these families in hospitals, in rehabilitation environments, and on school and community health teams. Julie's story raised my awareness and helped me become a more effective health care leader. It is a transformational tool that leads to a deeper understanding of the experience of families with medically fragile children, resulting in greater compassion, stronger empathy and the potential for improved capacity to support them."

~ **Chantal Krantz,** *RN, MScN, Manager, Connected Care, Children's Hospital of Eastern Ontario and Ottawa Children's Treatment Centre*

"*What I Would Tell You* continues in this revised edition to dive deeply into the heart of an unexpected parenting journey. Julie's compassionate and poignant storytelling creates a 'road map' making this book a must-read, touching on both the lightness and darkness of what unexpected plot twists in life grant you, and how you can cultivate resilience and hope along the way."

~ **Betsy Pilon**, *President, Hope for HIE Foundation*

"Julie eloquently captures the tough realities of parenting a child with medical fragility while also sharing the eventual beauty and joy that it can bring. In this revised and expanded edition, she openly and compassionately talks about the difficult topic of death and anticipating the death of one's child, a topic most of us prefer to avoid. Remarkably, this is not a gloom and doom story but rather one of hope, sprinkled with humour and an appreciation of the special moments when they occur. Julie's book is a must-have not only for the parents of children with complex medical needs but also the many different professionals who enter their circle of care. There is no better education than hearing directly from the parent themselves about this unique parenting experience and all that it encompasses."

~ **Barb Juett,** *Social Worker, Ottawa Children's Treatment Centre*

What I would tell you

One Mother's Adventure with Medical Fragility

REVISED AND EXPANDED EDITION

JULIE KEON

Foreword by Dr. Peter Humphreys

Merocea Publishing
Ontario, Canada

ISBN 978-0-9953333-0-7
Disability / Parenting

Printed in Canada

This book is dedicated with immense love to
my husband and fellow adventurer, Tim,
and our daughter, Meredith Ocea.

I also dedicate it in memory of Griffin Walker.

adventure*

noun ad·ven·ture \ əd-ˈven-chər \

1. an undertaking usually involving danger and unknown risks
2. the encountering of risks
3. an exciting or remarkable experience

* *Merriam-Webster Dictionary (merriam-webster.com)*

Contents

What I Would Tell You About Family Life

What I Would Tell You About Seeing the Bigger Picture

What I Would Tell You, the Professional

What I Would Tell You About Preparing for the Inevitable

What I Would Tell You About My Girl, Meredith

What I would tell you

Foreword

As Susan Sontag pointed out in her memorable 1978 book *Illness as Metaphor*,[1] to live with a severe, life-threatening disease is to live in a different, alien "Kingdom," far removed from the Kingdom of the Well. The same may be said for the parents and other family members of a child with a potentially fatal disease or severe neurologic disability. This assertion is nowhere better illustrated than in Julie Keon's remarkable book *What I Would Tell You*.

Julie describes how, following a sublime first pregnancy and home birth, she and her partner Tim were abruptly faced with a daughter (Meredith) who had sustained a severe perinatal brain injury that would lead to major permanent disabilities, a medically fragile state requiring long-lasting support from many health professionals, and the high probability of a shortened life-span. In describing for the reader how she and her family coped (and sometimes didn't) with the seemingly insurmountable task of living in this alien world of wheelchairs, tube feeding, sundry medications and visiting support workers, Julie has produced a model of wise advice and reassurance for other families with severely disabled and medically complex children.

What strikes you on reading this book is the way in which Julie has been able to make you feel the complex mixture of emotions and feelings that have pervaded the past 14 years of living with, and caring for Meredith: fear, exhaustion, bewilderment, excitement, frustration, anger, acceptance, pride in how much Meredith has achieved despite her disabilities, and above all love. The love that Julie and Tim feel for their daughter radiates from the printed page.

As a neurologist with many years of experience in the evaluation and treatment of children and adults with severe neurologic disabilities, I have come to know many of their parents and to witness their struggles with caring for their special child. Each family has found their own path, most often the one chosen by Julie and Tim, but sometimes having to surrender the care of their child – partially or in some cases completely – to foster families or to assisted living centres. Looking on from the outside, I had sometimes caught a glimpse of the reality of families having to live in a world that is so alien to what the rest of us experience. And through all those years of working closely with these families, those little glimpses were all I saw of that reality – until I read Julie's book. She has created, for "foreigners" like me, a clear vision of that world and the role of love in making it possible to survive and thrive in what seems, to the rest of us, to be a seemingly unbreathable atmosphere.

In this revised edition, Julie has added a significant amount of new material to the various sections of the first edition's text, material that helps amplify and extend the messages that she wishes to convey. In addition, however, the new edition concludes with a six-chapter section entitled *What I Would Tell You About Preparing for the Inevitable*. The section's chapters include an account of the manner in which Julie has gradually come to terms with the notion that she will very likely outlive her only child. There is wise advice on how to plan for a child's eventual demise and for the necessary events that follow; this advice is informed by Julie's experience as a certified Life-Cycle Celebrant. Particularly powerful are two chapters entitled "Savouring the Moment" and "One Day." The former is an eloquent description of the various "close calls" that occurred during the early years of Meredith's life and led to frequent and lengthy hospital admissions. This is followed by a passionate appeal – in part to herself, in part to the reader – to live in the moment. The latter chapter consists of a short poem in blank verse in which the author envisages a time when "…I once had a daughter." The message of this poem is universal; reading it brought me to tears.

For obvious reasons, health professionals play an important role in Meredith's story. Julie's numerous descriptions of encounters with health professionals of all stripes are very even-handed. Compliments and brickbats are handed out where appropriate. Health professionals caring for children with severe neurologic disabilities would be well-advised to pay particular attention to these descriptions, and to become better aware of some of the silly things we say in an otherwise well-meaning attempt to make parents "feel better." Reading *What I Would Tell You* reminded me again of the overarching importance of the following medical aphorism, an approach to medical care that I have tried my best to follow throughout my medical career:

Guérir quelquefois; soulager souvent; consoler toujours
(Cure sometimes; relieve often; console always)

Yes, as health professionals, we must always strive to console our patients and their families, especially when they are faced with an untreatable medical condition. But in doing so, we must try to understand the realities of the world in which they live.

In summary, not only is this book a vital resource for parents of children with severe, life-threatening neurologic conditions; in my opinion it should also be required reading for all health professionals who investigate, treat and follow such children. I would go further still. I believe that the overall message of Julie Keon's book, and the informed and sage advice contained therein, would be valuable to the parents of a child with a potentially life-threatening chronic disease (for example diabetes mellitus or leukemia), a child with a severe genetic neurodevelopmental disorder such as Down syndrome or Rett syndrome, or a mental health patient who has been physically or sexually abused in early life and whose still-developing personality has been shattered. All of these examples (and many more like them) share a common theme: parents and other caregivers are faced with some of the same long-term uncertainties, anxieties and turmoil that Julie and Tim have faced and repeatedly surmounted over the past 14 years.

Dr. Peter Humphreys, MDCM, FRCP(C)
Division of Neurology, Children's Hospital of Eastern Ontario
Professor, Department of Paediatrics, University of Ottawa

---

[1]Susan Sontag, *Illness as Metaphor*. New York: Farrar, Straus and Giroux, 1978

Acknowledgements

It seems appropriate that I start by thanking the person who inspired me to write the original essay *What I Would Tell You*, which ultimately led to my blog and this book. I may never know the name of the woman who was in the waiting area of the Children's Hospital of Eastern Ontario that day in June of 2011, but the brief interaction we had as I passed by her was the catalyst I needed to begin writing and sharing my thoughts and experiences. I often think of her and how she is doing. I wonder if she ever read *What I Would Tell You* and if she recognized herself in my writing.

All of the photographs featured in this book (except for two) including the front cover were taken by my talented husband and Meredith's father, Tim Graham (Tired Tim Photography). I am grateful that this passion was discovered and that he is naturally gifted in capturing moments and details through his lens. His photos have turned this into "our" book and so thank you, Tim, for your generosity and your eye in capturing the beauty in our everyday life.

I couldn't have embarked on the enormous task of revising and publishing this book without the tremendous team of family relief workers who help Tim and I care for Meredith. Thank you to Amanda who has been with our family for over twelve years and who has been a solid and dependable caregiver to Meredith. I thank our entire caregiving team (Sarah, Kelly and Erin) who have courageously learned the ropes of caring for our child with medical fragility, and who each bring their unique personalities, talents and creativity to our home and to Meredith. Their dedication has given me the space and time to focus on writing knowing that Meredith is cared for and is having loads of fun. And a shout-out to our night nurses, especially Jordan, who have allowed us to get restful sleep. It took ten years for us to get consistent sleep and we are grateful for their commitment, even when that means driving through a snowstorm to get here.

This revised edition needed a new cover and I wanted to find someone I could trust with such an important task. Janet Clarke bravely took on the role of graphic designer and layout expert, meticulously preparing the files

xiv

for print and overseeing all technical aspects of book publishing. Immense love and gratitude to Janet for understanding the enormity of this project and handling it with such care. Her gentle spirit helped me to feel excited and certain that I really could pull this off.

Having an excellent editor to polish the tarnished bits and make the new content shine was a labour of love! A big "thanks" to Matthew Godden (Thames Valley Wordworks) for his thorough and skilled editing of the final manuscript (leaving the blog in its unedited form). Thank you to my dad, Stan, and sister, Stephanie, who willingly and thoroughly read the edited manuscript to catch any typos, MIA commas and to make valuable suggestions. Your input brought even more clarity to this manuscript.

Thank you to the select few who read the first edition of this book and then agreed to read the manuscript of this revised edition providing their reviews: Andy Chrestman, Jennifer Cunningham, Barb Juett, Louise Kinross, Chantal Krantz, Betsy Pilon, Donna Thomson and Vania Oliveira. I value their time and their honest feedback. I am honoured by their kindness and heartfelt words.

I am enormously grateful to Dr. Peter Humphreys for his generosity in writing the foreword for this book and making time in his own very busy life to do so. Knowing that he is retiring from pediatric neurology right around the time of this book's release, makes his reflections that much more meaningful. Thank you for your support and for recognizing that this is a valuable read for professionals especially those just starting out.

I am so thankful to be surrounded by beautiful, strong women who encouraged and supported me when I considered bailing on this project for the second time. Thank you for helping me to remember who I am when I had forgotten. You know who you are.

Thank you to my family–both of origin and the one I gained in marriage. Thank you for believing in us and cheering us on as we navigate this parenting journey.

I would never have continued to write blog posts, and eventually this book, if it weren't for the many, many people from all over the world, parents and professionals alike, who reached out not only to read my offerings but to send emails and leave comments. Their feedback urged me to keep sharing my thoughts through the written word.

This book is the result of a deep love that began twenty-one years ago.

There is one person who has been by my side through it all. Without my husband and best friend, Tim Graham, Meredith would never have been. My heart is full of immense love for you, Tim. The first edition did not unfold as we had hoped and so I am grateful that you trusted me enough to let me lead the way when it came to publishing this version of my book. Most of all, thank you for carrying me when things didn't go as planned. Having your gentle strength to lift me up when I felt like giving up is the reason this revised edition exists at all. Walking this road together is an adventure that I would not change for the world. Seeing you father Meredith has been one of life's greatest joys. You are my one true love. I couldn't have done any of this without you.

And last, but most certainly not least, my life changed the moment I laid eyes on Meredith. I am grateful to her, my sweet girl, for her lessons, her wisdom, her patience and her unconditional love. Her life changed mine and it is my greatest hope that as a result we help others to understand.

Introduction

The last thing I ever imagined was releasing a revised edition of this book. In the three years that have passed since completing the first edition, I, naturally, have more to share with those who will benefit from my words. This edition contains the same nuggets of wisdom as the first, but I have added twelve new chapters, and the existing chapters have been updated.

When Meredith was born in 2003, my husband, Tim, and I somehow knew that allowing ourselves to fast-forward beyond the moment we were in would be detrimental to our well-being. The first 10 years of Meredith's life were like an extended postpartum period, and in some ways Tim and I can hardly relate now to the new mother and father that we were back then. Life has weathered and broken us down at times, but it has also brought us many lessons. We learned quickly that each time we faced a crisis head-on and leapt off the cliff of doubt and fear, we gained resilience and a renewed attitude of hope and gratitude. We became aware that this journey of parenting a child with medical fragility was nothing short of miraculous. It definitely had the potential to enhance our lives and change everything we thought we knew, in ways that we never could have imagined.

When I wrote the essay *What I Would Tell You* in June 2011, I received hundreds of emails and handwritten letters from all over the world. I recall one email in particular from a single mother of four living in rural Nebraska, U.S. Her youngest child had suffered a brain injury at birth. She told me that after reading *What I Would Tell You*, she felt someone finally understood her. She had always felt isolated, but now for the first time she didn't feel so alone anymore. That mother is one of the reasons I decided to write more extensively about my mothering experiences.

My hope has always been that this book would resonate not only with those intimately travelling this path, but also with the many professionals who come into contact with families like ours. Whether you are a mother, father, family member of a child with extra needs, medical student, doctor, nurse, occupational therapist, physiotherapist, teacher, educational assistant, family support worker, or any of the many other professionals that families like ours come into contact with, this book is for YOU.

But in fact, this book is for everyone, because there are so many misconceptions about what this experience is like for people like us. To this day, when I speak about Meredith with those who do not know us well, I am most often met with looks of pity and the dreaded words "I'm sorry," as though someone has died. Such people quickly assume that the most appropriate reaction is one of sympathy. I feel a sense of joy and relief when I share something about Meredith and I'm asked, "So, what does Meredith like to do?" or "Does she attend school?" or "What are her abilities?"

Being Meredith's mother for 14 years has been an awakening. Meredith has been, by far, my greatest teacher on my path through life. People often say how lucky Meredith is to have been born to two loving parents who care so deeply for her. Little do they know that we are the lucky ones! They have not had the privilege of growing beyond the very limited and stifling beliefs that I, too, once held about the world of parenting a child with extra needs.

Making the decision to release a revised edition of my beloved book was not easy. Sharing these very personal thoughts and words of wisdom with you has been challenging. It is my deepest wish that these words bring you comfort and clarity. If even one parent feels less alone by reading this book, I will feel gratified in having written it.

JULIE KEON
Ottawa Valley, 2017

What I would tell you
. . . about the early days

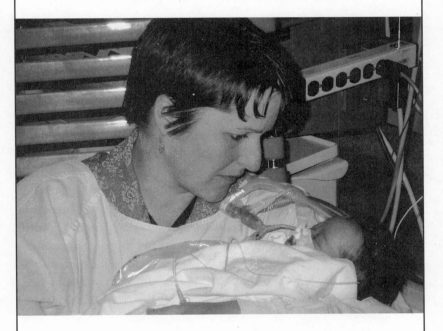

CHAPTER 1

Shooting the Messenger

December 5, 2004 7:23 p.m.: This is the exact moment, one year ago today, that Meredith Ocea Graham emerged from my body and started her life on the outside. The next six minutes following her birth were probably the most terrifying of our lives. I remember the voice of one of our midwives saying, "Speak to her, Julie and Tim. She knows your voices." The midwives were suctioning our wee girl and giving her oxygen as I stroked the sole of her foot and firmly demanded that she stay with us while telling her that we loved her and that she belonged here with us. And then I heard the words: "Call 911."

Six minutes after delivery, a large, burly man walked into this very sacred space and scooped our Meredith into his arms in a towel, then flew down the stairs and out the front door into the cold winter night and a waiting ambulance. Tim and I embraced, then he left to be with our girl. I, of course, stayed behind and slept at home surrounded by seven strong, beautiful women – my mother, my two sisters, our doula, our midwives and a dear friend. In the euphoria of post-birth endorphins, I had no idea what lay ahead. None of us did.

(From my personal journal)

Initially we were unaware of the extent of trauma that Meredith experienced at birth. We had been told by our doctors that since Meredith had survived the first 48 hours following her birth, we should start making plans to have her home for Christmas. On December 10th, we arrived at the hospital knowing that Meredith would be returning from a magnetic resonance imaging (MRI) test. We found her in her bed, under fluorescent lamps, looking obese compared to the other babies in the neonatal intensive care unit (NICU). She was full-term and weighed in at 7 pounds, 15 ounces (3,600 grams) while the majority of her roommates were significantly premature. They looked as though they had fallen out of a nest and were not quite ready to be on the outside.

My husband took a photo of me standing beside Meredith's bed. I often look at this photo and the woman in it as though it was the last piece of evidence of the old me. It was only moments after that picture was taken that the neurologist, who happened to be on call the night Meredith was brought in, walked into the room accompanied by a neurology student and a social worker.

He was a slight man with a kind, grandfatherly face. He had a beard, glasses and compassionate eyes, but I saw the sadness in them and thought to myself, "This is not going to be good news."

He said good morning and, in a very matter-of-fact yet so very gentle manner, explained that, as he had expected, the MRI showed that Meredith did indeed have a brain injury as a result of hypoxia. At one end of the spectrum, he said, she might be a clumsy child, and at the other end, she might have severe cerebral palsy (CP). Unfortunately, they were leaning more towards her being on the latter end of the spectrum.

The seconds that followed were a bit like a slow-motion film. An office chair was pushed up behind me causing my knees to bend, and consequently I collapsed into the chair. Then a box of tissues was placed in front of me in anticipation, I suppose, of the wailing that would surely follow this devastating news.

In the hallway or in the room that we shared with about five other families, it was not an uncommon sight to see parents collapsing in a heap when they learned that their baby was not going to be healthy or was not going to survive the night. It was part of life in the NICU.

But the tears did not come at that moment. I recall feeling sadness for this doctor who had come in to work that morning knowing that he had to break this terrible news to two new parents. His neurology student stood beside him, doing her best to remain professional and stoic. The social worker seemed afraid when she saw tears welling up in my eyes, and she ushered us off to a small room so as not to "disturb the other parents."

My husband and I cried then, in that small room usually reserved for babies who needed isolation or for excess furniture and medical equipment. There were a few chairs and windows all around, which the social worker hastily covered with blinds to give us some privacy.

I looked at my husband and through my tears said, "What are we going to do?" A wave of anxiety, or maybe even primal terror, washed over me as my mind was flooded with images of the adults I had spent time with in my youth. During the summers, I had assisted the activity director at a local nursing home. I remembered the residents who had CP. I fast-forwarded 25 years and thought to myself, "How are we going to do this? I will be an old woman caring for a severely disabled adult woman. My God, how did this happen?"

As quickly as we were overwhelmed with fear, we became very calm, a natural response to shock. We wiped our tears and pledged in that moment that this beautiful baby was going to have the best possible life. We were going to make sure of that.

My husband left to take a moment for himself, and I walked into the hallway to see my father coming toward me, excited to see his newest granddaughter. How heartbreaking to have to look at his joyful face and tell him what we had just been told: that this seemingly perfect baby was dealing with a very injured brain and that the life we had imagined and planned for her was no longer a possibility.

The hospital chaplain approached me and offered to pray with me or to call someone from my church. I remember staring through my angry tears and saying, "God and I are no longer on speaking terms."

We met the neurologist the next morning to talk more about Meredith's prognosis. He was a seasoned doctor and he knew that after the initial shock wore off, we would be able to absorb more information. He shared bits and pieces at a time to avoid overwhelming us.

During this meeting, he attempted to be positive about having a child with cerebral palsy. He explained that she would show us love in her own way and that it was not necessarily going to be a horrible existence from this point on. He asked us if we had ever seen the movie *My Left Foot*, starring Daniel Day Lewis. He described the outline of the movie and how convincing Mr. Lewis was in his portrayal of a man with spastic quadriplegic CP. All I remember thinking was, "So this man grew up to write a book with his foot? How in bloody hell is that comforting?"

In the days that followed, our neurologist would schedule times when he would come in to assess Meredith and talk with us. It did not take long to notice how urgently I would need to go to the cafeteria or the library to check email whenever one of his visits was scheduled. He would turn up at the planned appointment time to find my husband sitting alone with Meredith and he would suggest that they wait until I returned. My husband would reply,

"No, she won't be coming back for this appointment."

This behaviour continued even after we were finally discharged and sent home ten weeks after she was born. Our first neurology appointment as out-patients was a source of tremendous anxiety for me, but I could not avoid it any longer. I needed to accompany my husband and Meredith.

I really liked this man, but for some reason the thought of seeing him produced a sickening anxiety that I could not shake. It was not until Meredith was celebrating her first birthday that I confessed my odd behaviour to him at our scheduled appointment. I had finally figured out why I dreaded seeing him so much. He calmly told me that my reaction was normal and that he had seen it many times before. He was "the messenger" – the bearer of the worst news I would ever receive in my life. I associated him with that bad news.

Making this connection and sharing with him freed me from the grip of the paralyzing fear I had grown to expect in anticipation of our appointments. I was then able to see him as a person, a man, a father and a brilliant pediatric neurologist. He no longer represented that moment frozen in time when everything changed forever.

CHAPTER 2

Protecting My Mother Heart

Never have I felt more instinctual than when I was pregnant. If ever there was a time to listen to my body and trust its messages, this was it. If I was tired, I rested. If I was hungry, I ate. I gave in to cravings and avoided those things that made my stomach turn. I had spent years encouraging mothers to do just that, and yet I was unsure I would be able to practice what I preached when my time came. Being pregnant was a lesson in surrender, and I trusted that I would mother my baby by simply following my gut. If I was able to conceive and grow this baby to term, then it only made sense that listening to my inner guide would help me along the way as a mother.

When we discover that we are pregnant or learn that we will become parents through adoption, we spend time reading, researching and determining the best ways to do things. We make intelligent and informed choices. Will we ask a doctor or a midwife to assist? Will we plan for a home birth or a hospital birth? Will we breastfeed or formula feed? Will we co-sleep, attachment parent or do things the way our own mothers did?

We take special care of ourselves in anticipation of the arrival of this new being. In the wee hours of the morning, we may be plagued with thoughts that scare us awake: What if I'm a terrible mother? What if I don't love this baby? What if my partner and I can't handle the stress of parenthood? What if I get postpartum depression? These worries are a normal and beneficial part of anticipating the imminent arrival of a new family member. They force us to explore and face our deepest fears. They allow us to acknowledge things we usually tuck away and ignore in our day-to-day life. Pregnancy brings shadows into the light. We have months of gestation not only to grow a baby but also to grow ourselves. Any unresolved business will come to the surface in pregnancy, and if we continue to ignore it, it will likely make itself known during labour or in the weeks following. Pregnancy, birth and parenthood challenge us on all levels, and there are many lessons to be learned if we are willing to recognize them.

I imagined the birth of our daughter over and over in my mind. As a doula helping parents through the childbirth experience, I had been to 99 births when my turn finally came. I had a vast amount of material to choose from and add to my imagined birth experience. We planned a home birth. I daydreamed about the first moment I would lay eyes on our new baby. I imagined we would be bathed in pure love and joy. My husband and I would welcome our new baby into our lives and rejoice in the new life we had created. A new chapter would begin. We would be parents!

December 5, 2003 did not unfold quite as we had imagined. The labour was straightforward enough. I was up most of the night with mild contractions and called my chiropractor at 6:00 a.m. to come to our home and give me one last adjustment before things really picked up. He arrived at 6:30 a.m. and could feel our baby's legs high up under my rib cage. Once he adjusted me, the contractions increased in intensity and once they were coming every four minutes, I knew things were really starting to roll and we called our midwife. She arrived at 9:30 a.m. and assessed me to find that I was already four centimetres (4 cm) dilated. We called our doula, Tammy, as well as our friend Jessie, who was in charge of taking photos, to tell them that there would be a baby born on this day. My mom was also on her way to oversee the many tasks involved in a home birth. It was a beautiful winter morning with each fencepost, branch and twig covered in a blanket of sparkling frost.

I recall being amazed by the contractions, while at the same time being unsurprised by their intensity. As a doula I had witnessed first-hand, over and over, the sheer power of birth. I was in awe of the fact that I was actually labouring as opposed to supporting someone in labour. It was surreal to be on the other side of the experience.

As our care team arrived, everyone surrounded me with their strength and support. I remember feeling completely safe in the arms of my husband, Tim, and in the sacred space that the other women held for us. I spent most of the time labouring upstairs in the bathroom, which had a shower, a soaker tub and lots of space. At about 1 p.m., my membranes ruptured spontaneously, and our midwife announced that I was now 7 cm dilated and that we could anticipate our baby's birth by 3:30 p.m.

Labour progressed well. Tim never left my side, and I remember trying to convey to him the intensity of each contraction but being unable to speak. They were sharp and took my breath away, and I remember how helpless he appeared as he tried to find things to do to ease my pain. But even though I felt washed away with every rising contraction, I also felt grounded and strong, and not once did I feel the need for pain relief. With that said, I do remember thinking that I completely understood why women choose epidurals.

I anticipated spending most of my labour in our tub, but lying in it was excruciating. So I either stood or squatted in ankle-deep water instead. Around 3 p.m., I was 9.5 cm dilated with a stubborn lip of cervix that remained there until 5 p.m. This was the most challenging part of all: I experienced insane contractions, with the urge to push at the peak of each contraction. I panted my way through the urge to bear down, so as not to cause swelling on my cervix. We tried all kinds of positions and maneuvers.

Finally, after three hours, that lip moved out of the way, and I was finally able to give in to the powerful urge to push. Second stage began. By this time I was sitting on the birth stool in our master bedroom, and everyone had gathered close to encourage me through each surge. I was so astounded by the power of pushing. I couldn't believe how my body just took over, and I respectfully got out of my body's way to let it do its job. I will always remember Tim telling me that he couldn't believe how the muscles in my back would tense up and ripple with each contraction. There is nothing as magnificent as the incredible strength and endurance of birth.

By the time the baby's head started to crown, I had been pushing for just under two and a half hours. My doula helped me "pah-pah-pah" through the surges to gently ease the head out, and I distinctly remember thinking to myself how funny it was that I was the one birthing and not the one guiding a woman with the "pah-pah-pah's."

At 7:23 p.m., Meredith finally slipped out of my body into the hands of my mother: her Nanny. She sputtered and was placed onto the towels and bedding that had been laid out for her on the floor. At that time, I was on my hands and knees so I spun around to look down at our beautiful, black-haired baby. Oh, she was a beauty, and I couldn't believe we had a girl! I had been certain I was carrying a boy.

There was thick meconium around her head as it crowned. Meconium is the first bowel movement that the baby has, although sometimes they pass it in utero. This is not necessarily an emergency. When meconium appears suddenly as it did for us, it can indicate distress in the baby. Our midwives already had oxygen and suctioning set up, so they were ready to suction our baby as soon as her head was born. Our midwife firmly asked me to speak her name and to ask her to stay with us.

I called out, "Meredith, Meredith. You stay here with us. Do not leave us. We need you here."

Oxygen was administered. The emergency number 911 was called. A gigantic man walked into our bedroom, into our sacred birth space, and scooped up our dark-haired beauty. He ran down the stairs with our midwife bagging Meredith along the way, whisking her into a waiting ambulance on a cold December night. My husband left then to go with our baby. I remained at home, surrounded by my mother and sisters, our midwife, our doula and a dear friend.

I awoke abruptly the next morning at 5:00 a.m. and felt a desperate need to go to Meredith. I showered and dressed, and we drove into the city to the children's hospital. I was weak from birthing so I was wheeled into the hospital in a wheelchair and up to the NICU. My husband came out to meet us, and we looked at one another in shock and with love and concern. It was as though we had been in a train wreck. Our brains were trying to make sense of the last 12 hours and what exactly had just happened. I shuffled into the NICU as if drawn by some sort of magnet. I could not get to Meredith fast enough. And there she was, plump and beautiful with a head full of dark hair. Could this really be her? I grew this gorgeous being inside my body? I wanted to scoop her up and run away from this place. Meredith had tubes coming out of her mouth and nose, and even out of her belly button. She looked as though she too had been in a train wreck. We were told that some touching was allowed but that we must not overstimulate her. I reached in through the portal of the bassinet to touch her chubby thigh and tell her that her mama was here now.

I do not know when it happened exactly. At some point in those very early days, some part of me shut down. Having to walk out of that hospital every night and leave our newborn in the care of strangers contradicted my natural instinct. In order to survive, I had to shut down some part of my brain.

After we received the devastating news that Meredith was not going to recover and that she was not going to be "okay," I unconsciously decided to maintain some distance from her. That way, if she was taken from me, it might not hurt as much.

I could not have left her there every day for 70 days in a row if I had allowed myself to experience the full range of primal emotions of a new mother. I still cared for her as though her life depended on it, which as it turns out it did. I groomed her and held her close. I expressed milk every three hours around the clock for almost a year to give her what I felt was the most optimal nutrition. I gazed into her faraway eyes hoping to see some sort of glimmer showing that there was someone inside, but I did not allow myself to fully bond. I was her mother, but I was also her nurse, her therapist and her caregiver. I felt somehow that she knew I would come around in time.

Meredith was patient with me. It was as though she came from some magical place and understood that none of us really banked on life turning out like this. She understood that with time we would all find our footing. We had each other for support, and between the three of us there was enough love to sustain us through anything we encountered.

Over time I started to open up again. I realized that no amount of shutting down, denying our reality or keeping my baby girl at arm's length would protect my mother's heart, a heart bursting at the seams with tremendous love, grief, and the desire to protect. No one knew how long we had together. Armed with this awareness, I took the plunge and opened my heart fully, knowing that one day I would likely experience the greatest heartbreak of all.

CHAPTER 3

Hardwired to Defend and Protect

In the animal kingdom, "not-so-perfect" offspring, such as young born with congenital anomalies, an illness, or even a low birth weight (the runt of the litter) are ignored by the mother and are usually left to die. This is because the mother knows her young will not survive in the wild with their particular afflictions.

Thankfully, we *Homo sapiens* have evolved from this basic survival scenario. Our decisions at birth are not so cut and dried. I understand that a child who is ill, medically fragile or has significant extra needs is not always accepted. Some parents make the difficult decision to relinquish their parental rights and choose to place their child for adoption or in foster care as a form of protection for their child. I can only write about our particular situation, in which we did not consider the possibility of giving up our daughter. Instead, we scrambled to figure out how we would protect and assist our child who was expected to have a far more challenging time surviving and thriving in our society than her healthier counterparts.

We are hardwired to defend and protect our young. Sometimes that primal reaction can take a new parent by surprise. In my prenatal classes, I spoke about mother's instinct and the primal and protective forces that remain just below the surface of a seemingly calm and reasonable new mother. Nothing prepared me for the intense feelings of protection that brewed during my pregnancy and were activated at the moment of Meredith's birth.

I felt my Inner Mama Grizzly Bear (IMGB) rise up for the first time when Meredith was a mere five days old and had returned from an electroencephalogram (EEG). An EEG records the electrical impulses that the brain cells create when they communicate with each other. In order to gather this data, 15 to 25 electrodes are placed all over the scalp and attached with a sticky paste.

We arrived to find Meredith in her little plastic cave bed. Since there was a nurse at her side, we walked to the opposite side of the crib and watched as the nurse proceeded to vigorously rub Meredith's delicate furry head with a cloth. The nurse was attempting to get the sticky paste out of her thick head of hair. I had what can only be described as an out-of-body experience. In this hidden imagining, I scrambled over the container that held our daughter and pounced on the nurse who was manhandling my precious baby.

I was taken aback by my imagined scenario and knew at that moment that no amount of training or education as a doula could sedate the IMGB that was apparently alive and well within me.

Since then, my IMGB shows herself whenever I perceive a threat to my cub's well-being. I have had moments when I visualized a large bear paw coming out of nowhere and knocking the offender's head off in one fell swoop. I can then sit and nod and wait my turn to speak while calming myself with visuals of what I would be doing if I really was a mama grizzly bear. These images soothe both me and *her*.

I find it fascinating that the majority of those entrusted with the care of our most vulnerable members possess this primal urge to protect. And it is not only present in those who are biologically connected: parents who have received their children through adoption or fostering also develop this urge very quickly. Inner Daddy Grizzly Bears (IDGB) react just as strongly.

This primal feeling acts as an internal guidance system. It must be respected and trusted, but it must also be restrained somewhat to prevent us from acting on impulses that may not be socially acceptable.

CHAPTER 4

Having Hope

When I was 19 years old, I went on a two-month backpacking adventure through Western Europe with my older sister, Lana. At some point we separated and I met up with some locals in Leiden, Netherlands. What I remember most about that interaction was the poster that hung on the wall of their flat, which simply said: "The world's shortest pessimistic poem: *Hope? Nope.*"

My 19-year-old self loved it. I was leaving adolescence, but was still on a quest to "find myself." I was probably a bit of a pessimist at the time, or I may have found it hard to be joyful due to my anxiety about the future and what it held for me. I suppose I was basically hopeful, but my hope was always tinged with a good shot of fear about how my life would play out.

Although I was fearful about many things, I also had an underlying toughness. When things actually got difficult – as opposed to merely seeming difficult in my imagination – I responded very well. Although I feared sudden change and the loss of control, I was the person you wanted to have around in an emergency.

I remember hearing the word *hope* an awful lot in the early days and weeks after Meredith was born. Nurses, friends, family and even strangers would tell us that we "had to have hope." But what did that mean? At times, things felt absolutely hopeless. I had moments of believing that our lives would never, ever be okay again. It certainly didn't help that doctors were so very careful about their predictions, so as not to give us what they deemed to be "false hope." It was as if predicting a difficult future was considered far more appropriate and helpful than providing even a glimmer of hope.

Wikipedia defines hope as "an optimistic attitude of mind based on an expectation of positive outcomes related to events and circumstances in one's life or the world at large." So the concept of false hope didn't make a lot of sense to me. You are either hopeful or you're not. Preparing parents for various outcomes lets them know that anything is possible.

I recall a nurse in the NICU quietly telling us that we must never under-estimate the power of love in these situations. Even after all these years, that stands out to me as such a beautiful, hopeful message to give new parents. We didn't have much control over the future but we knew that we deeply loved Meredith and that she deserved to have parents who were, at the very least, cautiously hopeful.

With so much going against us, I understood why it was difficult for the doctors and other professionals to be optimistic and hopeful about our future. After repeatedly having our hopes dashed, it did seem far less disappointing to adopt a sense of hopelessness. But like so many things, being hopeful was a choice. Our lives were going to unfold anyway, no matter what we did, and we could choose to be in a state of hopelessness and disappointment, or we could approach each day with some semblance of hope. We chose to be hope-ful, cautiously so.

CHAPTER 5

Finding Signs of Life

Meredith's development has been slow...very, very slow. There is a comfortable, easy rhythm that comes with a child who does not change significantly over a good length of time. But sometimes, when we least expect it, something happens in that brain of hers that both surprises and amazes us. Meredith's beautiful, healthy brain was significantly injured in the moments following her birth, as a result of hypoxia. Her brain injury was so extensive and so "interesting" to the doctors that MRI scans taken when she was a mere five days old were shown to neurologists-in-training.

On December 10, 2003, the day we learned that our daughter's brain was significantly damaged by the hypoxic episode, we decided we would do whatever was needed to help her reach her full potential. We were determined to prove them all wrong, especially the pediatrician who coldly told us, "This is very serious. Do you understand that? Your daughter will never walk, talk, eat, communicate, and so on." I remember looking at that woman as I held this beautiful baby in my arms and visualizing myself leaping across the room and scratching her eyeballs out. These primal images both entertained the IMGB (Inner Mama Grizzly Bear) in me and kept me sane in those early days.

I will admit that there may have been some denial and some naïveté in the beginning, but we refused to assume that Meredith had no brain activity. We assumed that she understood what we were telling her. Had we listened to that pediatrician, we might as well have left her lying in a crib in the corner. Gradually, Meredith's brain started to heal, and we began to see signs that her brain was working. She would make a sad face if one of us left the room. She began to smile and eventually, she laughed. Over the years we have tried many things to help Meredith communicate with us. However, these attempts have been short-lived, as medical issues take precedence and she is unable to cope with anything more.

It was a glorious moment in July 2004 when I caught the corner of her mouth curling upward ever so slightly. I was certain that I was witnessing the beginnings of a grin, as profoundly subtle as it was. She was eight months old, and up until that moment I had been convinced that this little babe, who stared off into the distance and showed no enthusiasm about anything around her, would never smile. Her neurologist disagreed. He assured us that she would smile and even laugh…someday.

In August of that same year, we were having a lengthy stay at our local children's hospital. While our daughter slept, I tied a shiny Mylar balloon to the rungs of the metal crib where she lay. When she woke up, the metallic surface of the balloon caught her eye, and there it was…a wide, toothless grin beaming across her face. My husband walked in moments later, and I stood there exclaiming, "She's smiling. She's smiling!" He grabbed the camera and made a video clip. Over and over, we waved the balloon in front of her and she smiled. She actually smiled! This was more than a developmental milestone, it represented potential; it represented hope. It confirmed our instinctive feeling that she was aware of the world around her. We were not living in denial, as so many professionals seemed to think. She had a severe brain injury, but more than that, she had a soul that was starting to shine through.

Three years later, in response to a spontaneous kiss and tickle of her neck, she started to make a growling sound that quickly grew into a laugh. It took a tremendous amount of coaxing, but there it was. She was laughing! To this day, this child's sweet laugh can be a soothing salve for this mother's tired heart, fatigued body and restless mind.

I share this story because, while there is so much attention on what our children can't do, we need to focus on what they *can* do. I am not necessarily speaking of developmental milestones. We put a lot of pressure on ourselves and we worry about whether our child can hold their head up or whether they will roll over or sit independently. In the early days, we lived in that in-between world of "wait and see." Eventually, we made it to the solid, more predictable ground of "this is it." For us parents of children with a brain injury on the severe end of the spectrum, physical achievements are generally hard to come by.

This is why it is so important to pay attention to the subtler signs of your child's presence. Regardless of whether Meredith's brain resembled my own, I had to believe that beyond the lack of movement, the lack of sound and the blank stares, our girl's spirit lay right behind those eyes. I am not a religious woman, but having witnessed countless births and several deaths, I have come

17

to believe that we are made up of far more than simply organic material.

The human brain is a mysterious and complex organ. It is the control centre for all other functions of the human body. A brain injury, whether it happens at birth, from an accident or from other causes, is unique to that person, and the outcome is unpredictable to some degree. I have tremendous respect for neurologists, especially those who specialize in pediatric neurology.

"I am often reminded of the book, *My Stroke of Insight*, by Dr. Jill Bolte Taylor, a Harvard neuroscientist, who suffered a stroke at age 37. The entire left side of her brain was virtually wiped out. She lost her past, her future, her identity and her memories. Jill was only capable of being in the present moment and was no longer connected to the portion of her brain that made her an individual. She fully recovered eventually, and says in her book that when someone cannot speak or communicate due to an injury or dysfunction of the brain, we must believe they are still "there." Jill remembers being aware of other people's energy when she was in recovery and how she kept thinking over and over, "I am in here. Come get me. Come find me."

This is the way we have always viewed Meredith. We assume that her spirit is worth seeking, much to the chagrin of some experts. Had we assumed otherwise, she would not have blossomed as much as she has. Is this a guarantee that every child will do things that no one expected? No, of course not. We are all too aware that there are few guarantees. But I urge new parents, after the initial grief and shock have worn off, to do whatever they can to find the child who is hiding beneath the brain injury, the syndrome, the diagnosis. Although hard to find, that child is there. This, I can guarantee.

CHAPTER 6

The Dreaded "Wait and See"

If you are a newcomer to this adventure of parenting, I am certain you have some questions about how things are going to look for you and your child in the months and years to come. You may be asking questions like: When will I know what my child will be like? At what point do you know how "severe" your child will be? My daughter can hold her head up – does this mean she won't be as severe as your child? I am terrified that our son won't be able to do anything: what signs will tell me how bad things are?

If you have been asking these questions, I wish more than anything that there was a straightforward answer that could bring instant comfort to the very real anxiety experienced in these early days. That anxiety is so pervasive that it tends to dominate everything else – every thought, every emotion, every experience, everything. As much as we try to ignore these worries, they demand our attention and we desperately want to know something, ANYTHING, that will give us an inkling of what the future has in store for our little ones and consequently for us.

Let's be honest, though – what you're seeking are answers that will tell you your child won't be as severe as the doctors have predicted, and hopefully not as severe as some of the children you have seen on the countless groups you belong to on social media. It is terrifying to be launched into this world. As you start to look around and see the potential outcomes, that fear reaches whole new levels.

When we first heard those words – *severe cerebral palsy* – we felt panic and terror rise in us like hot lava. We couldn't begin to imagine what our future would look like. Our daughter was a mere five days old when we got the diagnosis. We'd only had five days to wrap our heads around the fact that we were parents, and now our dreams and expectations of parenting were coming to a grinding halt.

When we got this prognosis, my husband read medical journals in search of some glimmer of hope that things would be okay. It is different now, with social media. Parents find their way to public groups on Facebook and plead with the parents who are further down the road to assess the video clip they have posted and tell them if they think their child will be able to walk or talk or at least be less than severe. It's complicated because for the most part, they are told they just have to wait and see; that they just need to love their baby as they are right now. This is true but easier said than done. And still, as a newcomer to this land, you want answers – some measure of hope to hang onto as you navigate these early days.

The veteran parents, like me, try to comfort and console. I want to assure you that it won't always be this hard and terrifying, but I know my words would fall on deaf ears.

Newcomers to this land know what they are looking for, and if you aren't providing it, they don't want it. This reaction is neither right nor wrong; it's just a part of this adventure. I vividly recall searching for the same answers. I believed that if we worked hard enough and prayed hard enough that the outcome would be different. I wish I could go back and wrap my arms around that mother who was bound and determined to set those doctors straight for saying that Meredith would be as complex as she eventually turned out to be. I smile thinking back to my determination to somehow change the expected outcome. I realize now it is a part of this whole journey.

I listened to the stories of miraculous outcomes and of the ones who proved those doctors wrong. I didn't want to hear about anything else. I needed to know that there was always a chance that our girl would be that miracle and that one-in-a-million kid who baffled her doctors. And usually, when these questions are asked, there are the comments that boost the hopes of parents. They often start with "The doctors said our son wouldn't be able to do anything, and look at him now. [Picture posted of child]" Others tell you not to give up and to believe in miracles.

agonal breathing. acute neonatal encephalopathy. hypoxic ischemic. prognosis guarded. extraaxial T1 hypersensitivity. extraaxial hematomas. extraaxial hemorrhage posterior to left occipital lobe. cerebral edema. multiple signal abnormalities. widespread areas of ischemia. patchy heterogeneous echogenicity. small subdural bleed. diffuse brain edema. These are some of the words sprinkled throughout the initial paperwork of assessments when Meredith was just days old. Big, scary words that initially left us wondering what exactly becomes of a person with hypoxic ischemic encephalopathy, et cetera.

Gazing at Meredith's newborn face took almost all of my worries away. "And so what are we going to do then?" I thought. "You have a lot going against you, kid, but you have us and we love you no matter what."

It wasn't until Meredith was ten years old that I requested the original paperwork from those early days. We went by verbal descriptions of Meredith's diagnosis in the beginning, and it never occurred to me to ask to see it all written down in black and white. Upon my request, I was sent the results of the ultrasound of her brain and the MRI findings from when she was five days old, among other admission and discharge reports that I requested. I knew that our daughter suffered a massive brain injury at birth. That was clear. I never understood how profoundly she'd been affected by that injury until I read through the findings from the MRI, as well as the detailed notes hand-written by the man who has now been Meredith's neurologist for the last 14 years. He wrote about a 15-hour-old female who was admitted to the children's hospital's NICU in the early hours of December 6, 2003.

Had I accessed these reports then, I am not sure if I would have gone into mothering Meredith as instinctively as I did. Perhaps I would have deemed it hopeless and unnecessary to bother at all. These words that are forever etched on these pages confidently claim the most probable future for Meredith. The pediatrician tried to warn us of what was to come, as though that would ease the unfolding of the days yet unborn.

After reading the words in the report, my first thought was, "Oh my goodness, Meredith has some serious brain damage going on." This was followed by laughter as I watched Meredith sitting on her daddy's lap in her owl pajamas, vibrating with bliss as he played with her. I thought of all of the glorious years we have had and the sheer joy and depth of her living. I realized they are only words. Words do not define a person nor can they confine a spirit.

I am grateful I was not interested in these summaries and clinical reports initially. By not knowing in detail what we were dealing with, we were free from the limitations starkly communicated by these words. We were free to wait and see how this little flower would bloom on her own time and in her own way.

I firmly believe that motherhood (along with fatherhood) is the greatest lesson in surrender. Mothering a child with extra needs and medical fragility is an even greater lesson in surrender. This is the hard, cold truth:

There is no way of knowing when or how your child will reach their milestones, if at all. There is no way of knowing who your child will become.

But as you try in vain to figure out something that cannot be figured out, something magical happens. It is subtle, and it's hard to pinpoint the moment when the magic occurs, but one day you are going to notice that you are not thinking about the future as much. There will come a time when you won't compare your child to other kids with the same condition. You will even get to a place where you will no longer look at neuro-typical kids of the same age as your child and feel a piece of your heart snap off like a piece of peanut brittle.

Eventually, your son or daughter will just be who they are. It will happen in time, but being in the meantime feels like a slow suffocation. It is hard. REALLY hard. Chest-tightening-suck-the-breath-out-of-you hard. No one can give you the answer you seek. We can give opinions, share stories and give some hopeful comments, but none of us knows what tomorrow will hold.

Celebrate the great big things – like a hint of a grin, a peaceful sleep, the lifting of a head during tummy time. For some of us, this includes having our child with us one more day. Stay in that moment and celebrate big-time! Whatever the outcome, your child will amaze you in a way you cannot even imagine.

That, I do know. And you will know it, too.

CHAPTER 7

Finer Than Fine

She'll be fine ...

I heard this statement more times than I can count after Meredith was born. A broad, hopeful statement announced with such confidence that for many, it would override the grim prognosis given by the neurologist. Sometimes it was peppered with additional claims like, "Oh, she is so beautiful. She'll be fine" or "Lots of kids are a bit delayed. She'll be fine" or "The doctors don't know what they're talking about. She'll be fine."

I am still not certain if the ones saying this actually believed it, or if they were just trying to be positive in a very negative situation. They might have truly thought that cuteness was a measure of how a baby will turn out. This is reflective of another belief: that with enough love and prayers, miracles can happen. The problem with that is, when miracles don't happen, you can't help but wonder if perhaps you had loved a little harder or prayed a little more, things would be different.

I leaned more towards the knowledge and experience of our neurologist. I would nod and smile at those who said, "She'll be fine" with such gusto and sureness that I couldn't bear to shatter their dreams for our daughter. I would lead them to believe that I, too, knew she would be fine. The thing was, I knew the complete opposite was true. She wasn't going to be fine. In fact, she was going to be far from fine. She wasn't going to talk or walk or eat or dance or skip or sing or hug or do a great number of other things. The one thing I knew for sure was that our girl was *not* going to be fine. The mere fact she was still living was our miracle, and I knew that this would likely be the biggest miracle of all – the fact that she survived her birth.

"She'll be fine" was expressed in an almost patronizing fashion. Beneath "She'll be fine" was *"Quit being such a worrywart. Let's not entertain the reality of what you're dealing with. You are such a drama queen. Seriously, she'll be fine."* It was often punctuated with the flip of a hand. And I usually felt like maybe I *was* overreacting – maybe she would somehow, with enough hope and faith and prayer, be fine.

Over time, we realized that all of those people from the early days were right!

I have rarely been wrong when it comes to Meredith, but all those people who brushed off my concerns and worries with a flippant "She'll be fine" were right all along. I do know, though, that their version of "fine" was very different from what "fine" has come to mean in our lives. Back then, "fine" meant she would fully recover: she would be neuro-typical and even "normal" (whatever that means) and "okay." It was an attempt to ease our worries and invalidate our concerns.

Look up the meaning of "fine" and you will discover that it means "of high quality" and is associated with words like: *excellent, first-class, first-rate, exceptional, outstanding, superior, splendid, magnificent, exquisite, select, supreme, superb and wonderful.*

"She'll be fine"? You bet she will. She is finer than fine.

What I would tell you
. . . about the need for support

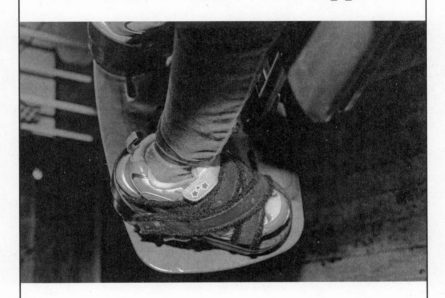

CHAPTER 8

Self-Care

One of the most valuable lessons I learned as a doula was the importance of self-care. I spent several years on-call awaiting the buzz of my pager which would signal the beginning of a labour and the birth that would soon follow. This meant many sleepless nights, disruption of plans and a constant state of readiness. Part of my role as a professional guiding and supporting couples through labour was to be available, dependable and consistent. I made sure to care for myself so that I could provide excellent care to the new mother and her family. Regardless of what was going on in my life, I left my personal problems at the door and made sure that I was physically and mentally healthy enough to endure the sometimes seemingly endless hours of labour.

I also taught mothers and fathers how critical it was for them to do all they could to ensure their own health. It is the responsibility of the parent(s) to stay healthy in mind, body and spirit so they are capable of caring for their child or children. Once they become parents they no longer have the luxury of crawling into bed to hide away from the world when they feel ill or exhausted. They have to do everything possible to get well and stay well for the sake of their children. My friend, Susan, who is also a doula, uses the analogy of being on an airplane when travelling with children. In an emergency, we must put on our oxygen masks first and then assist our children with their masks. If we fumble we may risk losing oxygen ourselves and passing out. As parents in real life, we need to follow the same advice.

Self-care can be a tricky subject precisely because it's not rocket science. In our society there is no shortage of information – from television shows featuring real-live doctors dishing out advice, from magazines and newspapers, and of course, from the Internet. We all know that eating well, exercising, quitting smoking, getting enough sleep and reducing stress are keys to health and well-being, and yet most of us store that knowledge away and never actually apply it.

When I was pregnant with Meredith, my husband quit smoking "cold turkey" on Father's Day as a commitment to our unborn baby. He was successful for six months, until the night she was born. The new habit of being a non-smoker could not compete with the trauma and stress of those moments after her birth. My husband found solace and relief in a cigarette. It wasn't until Meredith was six years old that he made a decision to quit again. His motivation was still Meredith, but this time he wanted to make sure he stayed healthy because without him, I would likely be unable to care for her. He couldn't bear the thought of that and quit a habit that had been a part of his life for 25 years.

For me, being healthy and resilient for the long haul was my motivation. I wanted to be the best I could be when it came to caring for Meredith. I needed to practice what I had preached to my prenatal students and expectant parents when I worked as their doula.

When you become the parent of a child with extra needs, self-care takes on a new urgency. We are under tremendous pressure to stay well because we are the primary caregivers, and cannot easily drop our children off at the neighbour's house or have family members step in to provide care. We are under tremendous amounts of stress and are often chronically sleep-deprived. It is natural to rely on stimulants like coffee and sugar, high-carbohydrate diets, and alcohol to keep us going – which works for a while but gradually becomes less and less effective. It can wind up becoming a vicious cycle of mood- and energy-boosting followed by a crash and the need for more stimulants to bring our mood and energy back up.

The human body was not designed to experience long periods of intense stress. Eventually it takes a toll on us, either mentally or physically, or both. Many parents struggle with depression and anxiety on top of chronic ailments, like generalized pain and insomnia, and stress-related issues like skin disorders, digestive and gut problems, and headaches. Our immune systems become taxed and susceptible to auto-immune disorders, cancers and general illness. It is not uncommon to place our own needs on the back burner, as most of our time becomes dedicated to endless appointments, precise routines and just caring for our children day and night.

How to cope with all of this? Because of the havoc stress can wreak on our physiology, many parents rely on medications to help manage the side effects of stress –blood pressure medication, anti-depressants, anti-anxiety pills, sleep aids, and so on. Another option to consider is seeing a naturopath, if you are open to it and have access to one. A naturopath can suggest ways to alleviate or reduce symptoms in a more gentle and natural way, avoiding the side effects of medications.

Good-quality food usually supplies all the nutrition we need, but when the body is taxed from too little sleep and too much stress, supplements that are traditionally helpful in strengthening your body's ability to cope with stress can be useful.

I could never have managed to hold our daughter for over eight hours each day for over a decade without enlisting the help of a chiropractor and a massage therapist. Although we have never had a large income, we chose to make sacrifices in order to care for ourselves. We place high value on our physical and mental wellness. It means we drive older vehicles, don't go on vacations and don't have any excess income to play with.

Chiropractic and massage therapy have not only helped me physically but have been critical in keeping me well mentally. Chiropractic care supports the nervous system, and there were times when one simple adjustment would cause an emotional release. This can feel like having a mental and physical tune-up. Massage therapy is a tremendous stress-reducer, and one hour of lying still in semi-darkness while listening to the soft music they usually play in massage therapy clinics is worth every cent. It has been a gift to myself that has allowed me to be a much better mother and partner.

Although most people cringe when they hear the word "exercise" (I know I do), I can't discuss self-care without mentioning its healing benefits. After some fairly significant weight gain by the time Meredith was three years old, I knew I had to make some serious choices. I had a nutritional assessment done and joined a gym where I attended a boot camp class twice per week. I adjusted my eating habits and the weight came off. I felt better physically, but more importantly I experienced a huge shift in my mental state. I could see that exercising and eating well affected my mood. Losing twenty pounds off my small frame certainly helped, but what was most empowering was simply doing something for myself.

After a few years of boot camps and regular running, I developed some health issues and had to stop abruptly. In those early years, hard-core exercise and distance running was something I could do, but the years of carrying Meredith over my shoulder, along with sleep deprivation and high levels of stress, took their toll. As I close in on the midway point of the second decade of mothering Meredith, I have had to adjust my exercise regime to my abilities. I try to commit to doing something active three or four times per week. It is a lofty goal, and sometimes a week will pass without any exercise. Life and other commitments regularly get in the way. The important thing is to keep on trying.

While exercise has been shown to be an antidote to stress, extreme exercise can add more stress to an already over-taxed body. If you listen carefully, your body will guide you. If the thought of joining a gym overwhelms you, stick to what you know. Just go for a walk. Even if you can only manage two walks per week, do that. Just start slowly and increase as your life and abilities allow. With some imagination and creativity you can fit fifteen minutes of some sort of activity into your day. I have enjoyed purchasing exercise programs that require little equipment and that I can do at home before Meredith wakes up. I do best when I have a schedule to follow. I am often found jumping around in Meredith's room while she lies on her futon and grins at her old mother doing her exercises in pajamas and running shoes.

Our children have teams of professionals to manage the medical challenges, and to provide diagnoses and support. We also need to create a team of healthcare providers to oversee all aspects of *our own* health. I knew right away that Meredith's birth was a "biggie" in my lifetime of experiences, and so I embarked on therapy when I was just six weeks postpartum. I just had this feeling that if I did not process the first six weeks – as well as have a wise and objective person to assist me in dealing with the ongoing unexpected twists and turns – I would either end up having a mental breakdown at some point or be forced to go into counselling years later in search of the feelings and experiences I had buried in those early weeks. Neither of those appealed to me!

Though you might not need to see a counsellor or therapist regularly, seeing someone as soon as possible and building a trusting relationship can be one of the best steps you can take in self-care. You may see a therapist for three months and then feel strong and settled enough to take a break. As issues arise, you may find that dropping back in to see your therapist can provide the guidance you need in that moment. When we were told our daughter had a short life expectancy, I was on the phone to my counsellor the next day. Whenever we have had big challenges or close calls or I find myself losing my footing, I know it's time for a visit to let it all out. We couldn't really afford therapy – but we also couldn't afford the fallout if we didn't find a place for decompressing and unwinding after weeks or months of holding it all together for our child, our spouse, family, friends, nurses and all the other professionals. Many organizations and agencies that work with families like ours have social workers on staff that parents can access at no fee or for a minimal fee.

Some therapists do pro bono work. It can be worthwhile to call around and explain your situation to see if you can get therapy on a pro bono basis. Try to find someone who specializes in perinatal loss, birth trauma, medical fragility or whatever your unique situation might be. I learned a long time ago that when new things arise that rock my foundation, a few sessions with my counsellor can help me to process the complicated feelings and get me back into focus on this present moment.

Caring for yourself also includes learning to ask for help, and learning to say "no" when you just cannot add any more to your plate. Asking for help is tough. It's even more challenging if asking for help is your only option.

Neighbours, members of your church, colleagues, family and friends are usually willing to do what they can to assist you, but you must take the first step. People cannot help if they are not aware that you need help in the first place or if they do not know your specific needs. Think of a few tasks that would make life easier for you: last-minute pickups of medications at the pharmacy, a drive to an appointment, help with childcare if you have other children, help with mealtime, or even bringing over meals. Be creative. When someone says, "Just let me know if I can do anything to help," jump all over that. Be ready to reply with suggestions. If you just say, "Sure, thanks, I will," you know (and they know) you never will. Find the courage and confidence to delegate.

When someone says, "Just let me know if I can do anything to help," you can reply, "You know what would really help me? We find Wednesday evenings almost unbearable, as my husband works late and Shauna needs to get to her dance class and Bobby is late getting off the bus. Would you be able to bring supper over some Wednesday night?" or "Would you be able to take Shauna to her dance class?" or "It would be so helpful if you could just be here when Bobby gets off the bus and stay with him until I get home." You get the idea.

A burned-out parent is not a useful parent. If you refuse the help, you also take away an opportunity for someone else to feel good about offering their services, whatever they may be. I once had a massage therapist offer me several complimentary massages, as she could see the pain I was in and she knew we were strapped financially at the time. What a gift she gave me! Was it easy for me to accept her generous offer? Absolutely not – but life works in such beautiful ways that I was able to help her down the road with something in her life. It all comes around. We are not meant to do this all alone. If we were, we would have been given a pair of colourful tights and a cape.

Learning how to say "no" can be challenging. I've found two ways to forgo the things that drain me as opposed to those that sustain me.

First, when someone asks me to do something, whether by phone or email, my automatic response is "Let me think about it and I will get back to you." Memorize this one-liner. It will save you from agreeing to many unwanted commitments. How many times have you agreed to do something, to take on one more task, only to kick yourself afterward? As if you didn't have enough in your life to deal with!

Secondly, when I'm not sure I want to commit at all, I remember this very important phrase: "When in doubt, don't." I first heard Oprah use this on her TV show many years ago and it stuck with me. It has been a simple but effective way to weed out the things I cannot, or don't want to, take on.

What used to be stressful to me before Meredith was born would be a walk in the park today. So much of our stress comes from our perception of things, yet the stressors of raising a child with medical fragility are real and unavoidable. I recall a discussion we had in one of my parents' groups about self-care and prevention of chronic stress-related ailments and illnesses. Listening to these parents talk made me realize that there is only so much we can do. If we have funding for night nursing, we get a few nights of full sleep. If the night nurse cancels, we don't. Self-care doesn't mean you just go to bed anyway. Somebody has to look after your loved one.

If you are just starting out on the path of being a parent of a child with extra needs or medical fragility, there is a lot you can do now. Be vigilant in your self-care and forget about everything you ever believed about asking for help. There are no medals handed out on this path. Being a martyr will only bring you closer to ill health either mentally or physically or both.

This road is mostly uphill, with terrain that will challenge you every step of the way. You are the only person who can save you, because your spouse, if he or she is still in the picture, cannot cope with more. Everybody else, except for maybe a handful of empathetic friends and family members, eventually gets on with their lives and they, too, have enough on their own plates.

If you are further along on this road and have evaluated your own self-care practices only to receive a very low score, it is never too late. Even small changes can yield big results in the long run, such as resilience, a strong immune system, a happier mood and a greater ability to cope with stress. The more you care for yourself, the easier and more natural it becomes.

Caregiving is not for the weak. We must grow and develop into long-term caregivers who can withstand the trials and hardships that are sure to come our way. Practice preventative healthcare so that you do not crumble under the strain of the realities of your life. It is more than possible: it is *necessary*, and the choice is up to you. Begin now.

CHAPTER 9

Getting Through the Tough Days

I can tell you with certainty that there will be tough days ahead. Describing them as "tough" might be sugar-coating reality. You may have days that you really, truly believe you cannot get through. These are the days you are 100 per cent sure you will not be able to cope for one more minute. Everything is falling apart at once, and the overwhelming stress and anxiety, compounded by tremendous sleep deprivation, may sweep you away. You believe that THIS IS IT, the final day of your sanity and your ability to cope. But by some miracle and by the seat of your pants, you will get through it.

It may take time for you to come to a place of trust in this process. After the umpteenth time of believing that you cannot handle it, you will emerge knowing that no matter how hard it gets, you will get through it one way or another. You will.

Is it necessary to reach out to others for help? Absolutely. Do you need to let out a desperate wail to blow off steam? For sure. Should you stomp around, vent and have a pity party in the midst of the crisis? Yes. Will you say things you might regret later? You might, but try to be gentle with yourself, acknowledging that you deserve a moment of madness. These moments of falling apart will be your saving grace in the long run. It is better to have mini-breakdowns, or breakthroughs as I prefer to call them, than to keep feelings pent up for months or even years at the risk of releasing it all in one disastrous moment.

Sometimes we have warnings that tough days are just around the corner, such as when your child starts to display telltale signs of distress. When difficult surgeries are scheduled, we can prepare ourselves to some degree and plan to function in survival mode for the duration. There are times, though, when things take a sudden turn and what seemed like a normal day rapidly becomes a crisis. It is good to have an emergency preparedness "kit" around. First and foremost, the strong listening ear of a non-judgmental person is critical in emergencies. You might also find that a fast-paced walk, a hot cup of tea and deep breathing are helpful. These remedies can be used anytime you feel the day is unravelling and you know it is going to be a tough one.

A few times a year, we make the long journey to our community's children's hospital. For the first eleven years, travelling with our daughter was akin to being thrown into a pit of angry fire ants. There was no escaping the screaming, panic-stricken, psychotic state of our child strapped into her car seat. It took self-control to convince ourselves to stay on the road and not steer abruptly into a tree to change our situation. I might be exaggerating just a little here, but there were times when that 100-kilometre drive felt like a never-ending hell ride on the crazy train. The worst appointments involved a visit to the dental clinic. After that horrific drive, we then straddled our daughter and forcibly held her down so strangers with masks could prod her with sharp instruments. After surviving this traumatic experience, she would once again be strapped into the car seat for the drive home- all told, four hours of pure hell. Although not my toughest days, these were days I dreaded and loathed.

There may be periods in your child's life when the tough days seem endless. These may turn into tough weeks, which, by the way, seem far more common in the early years. We spent eight months of Meredith's first year in the hospital. While you may manage to remain hopeful even during the tough days, when those tough days start to go on and on, you may wonder if there will ever be another "normal" day. This is where the support of family and friends, a therapist and your Internet groups come in. They can cheer you on and allow you to vent, which may give you the strength you need to keep going. Ideally, on the tough days there will be short periods of time when you can rejuvenate (without guilt!) and take a mental health moment. Having periodic mini-breakdowns can help release the pressure that builds up in your body. The more tough days you endure, the more resilient you become. We are hardwired to survive.

CHAPTER 10

"Yabut" and the Art of Support

In the prenatal education course I used to teach, I dedicated a generous portion of time to the topic of unexpected outcomes and difficult births. It wasn't my intention to be a downer and spread doom and gloom over an expectant couple's hopeful and, oftentimes, idealistic visions of their upcoming birth. I simply wanted to add a dose of reality, offer clarity on what's involved when a birth is perceived as difficult or traumatic and, most importantly, help them learn what to do if they found themselves feeling sad, disappointed, or angry about their birth experience.

I also created a workshop for women whose birth experience had left them feeling traumatized to one degree or another. They may have been planning a home birth and ended up being transferred to the hospital for a caesarean birth. Sometimes, a woman is traumatized because the birth was so fast that the baby's head was crowning before she could process what was happening. Women who plan to have pain management such as an epidural can feel ripped off when forced to give birth naturally due to staffing shortages or a precipitous labour. What causes trauma in one woman may have little effect on another.

The problem with unexpected outcomes in birth, including birth trauma, is what happens afterward. Some common responses to a woman attempting to share heartbreak over her birth experience are: "Yabut if you didn't have the caesarean, who knows what could have happened?" "Yabut having a fast birth is so much better than having a 40-hour labour, right?" "Yabut imagine what would have happened if he had been born at home as you had planned." Probably the most common response to a woman's attempts at sharing her birth story is: "Yabut AT LEAST THE BABY IS HEALTHY."

I've coined a word to describe this syndrome: "yabutting." Any and all "yabutting" is unhelpful and usually causes the mother to feel guilty for feeling the way she does, especially if her baby is healthy. When you reply to a person with "Yabut (fill in the blank)," you are invalidating how they feel. Trust me,

I KNOW that having a healthy baby is MOST important. I get that. And so does the mother you are talking to. She can feel grateful to have a healthy baby and at the same time feel sad about how her baby was born. It does not have to be one or the other. In fact, having a baby gives rise to all sorts of conflicting and complex feelings.

"Yabutting" also spills into other areas of life. There may have been times when, as a parent of a child with extra needs, your frustration was met with the old "Yabut there is always someone worse off than you" or "Yabut you really need to focus on the positive things."

I am a positive person. I tend to see the glass as half full as opposed to half empty – and yet, I also allow myself the odd pity party. I allow myself to let go once in a while, venting and purging the things I wish were different. Do I need to have these thoughts and feelings cancelled out by "yabuts"? No. What I do need in these moments is the ear of a friend or family member who trusts that I am doing some good old-fashioned mental housekeeping. I need the support of someone who knows me well enough to know that I *do* see that others may have a harder time than me, that my situation could always be worse than what I am experiencing now, and that I am grateful for the many, many blessings in my life. I need the support of someone who understands that I need a moment to unload and clear out the negativity that creeps in once in a while. I do not need my thoughts and feelings invalidated by "yabuts."

If you are with a friend or family member who is sharing their innermost feelings, refrain from "yabutting." Simply nod to show you are listening, and that will be enough. Listening is a skill that many of us failed to learn as we grew into adults. Some people try to listen but are distracted by the next question, comment or piece of advice that is whirling around in their minds waiting to be released. Some people share their stories that relate to the one you are expressing, therefore taking the attention away from you and putting it on themselves. This is a normal response to recognizing oneself in another's experience. Remember that although we may experience similar things, our perceptions and reactions will be as varied as the people who experience them. It is rarely a good idea to support someone by saying, "I know exactly how you feel."

When listening, it is natural to want to gather more information from the person who is talking by interrupting with questions to bring clarity. It is also normal to automatically search for helpful things to say because let's face it, we want to feel useful and fixing someone else's pain is a great place to start.

In the birth trauma workshops I offered, each woman was given the opportunity to share her birth story from start to finish without any interruption. Sometimes, especially during the most harrowing parts of the story, she would break down and be unable to continue. Instinctively, the listeners would be tempted to jump in and offer comfort or words of advice or hand her a tissue. Following my lead, they remained in silence, as this was a guideline we had agreed upon for this part of the workshop. It was interesting to observe the discomfort people felt simply holding space for the woman talking. No one was permitted to speak, and after a few seconds, the storyteller would catch her breath and continue on with her story. This part of the workshop was perhaps the most healing thing that we did over the two sessions, not only for the storyteller, but for the other participants who had to sit silently (uncomfortably) in the pain of another. When the person sharing looks to the listener for feedback, it is okay if nothing profound comes to mind. Sometimes, the best and most understanding thing to say is, "I don't know what to say."

Having even one person you can count on who understands the importance of listening non-judgmentally, can be all that you need to carry you through the hardest times. If everyone you trust fails miserably at supporting you, it is okay to educate them and let them know what is most helpful to you.

Most people will be grateful to have some gentle guidance from you. You may discover that even after offering guidance, you are met with clichés or less-than-helpful responses. I remember one relative used to say, "Well, it could be worse." This was true, yet in my moments of despair I didn't give a rat's ass about anyone else who might be dealing with far worse circumstances. And so, my reply to this person was, "Yes, things can always be worse, and reminding me of that only invalidates what I am going through."

Things can always be worse and things can always be better. Being supported wherever you find yourself on the spectrum of "for better or for worse" is what is required. If that means sitting in silence to avoid the "yabuts," the clichés, the invalidating comments, then ask for it. Think of what it is you need, and come up with a mantra to say to anyone who is courageous enough to step into the darkness with you. It could be, "It is most helpful for me to sit in silence with someone so that I can cry and vent uninterrupted." Just keep repeating this until the person who is attempting to support you hears it loud and clear.

Years have passed and I still recall those who held my hand when I stumbled and believed I could not go on. Don't forget to thank those who figure it out and become a lifeline to you on the toughest days. They are shining lights in our darkness and can make all the difference.

CHAPTER 11

Dealing with the Masses

You have probably discovered by now that just about everyone seems to have had bestowed upon them wisdom that you apparently missed – because every one of them wants to share with you the same annoying tidbits, as though they are handing you the secret to the universe. "Masses" refers to all persons other than your immediate family whom you will run across. The "masses" include members of your extended family, friends, strangers, neighbours, school officials, the professionals involved in your child's life, the lady who works the cash at your local store, your hairdresser, your co-workers and, well, everyone you might come in contact with while out with your child. Many assume you are the first to be enlightened with their particular aphorism. There are many aphorisms. These are my favourites:

1. "God only gives these special children to special moms."
Perhaps the intention of this comment is to make me feel like the chosen one. The truth is, many children end up in foster care because their parents were unable to care for them. Were these parents less special than me? People deal with extraordinary circumstances and try as they might, lots of parents are left with no choice but to relinquish their parental rights. Although I understand why someone might think it is appropriate to say this to parents like us, in most cases it is far from comforting.

2. "God only gives you what you can handle."
This is one of those well-intentioned comments that people make on a regular basis. I have learned that some days, we are given more than we can handle, and that by reaching out and accepting support and help from our families, friends, relief workers, therapists, physicians and the community, we are able to cope. I suspect a higher power isn't spending time watching and wondering if I might be able to handle just a bit more, just enough to have me teetering on the edge

of madness. If anything, I suspect that God (however you define something greater than us) carries me sometimes when the going gets really tough.

3. "This will make you stronger."
To which I reply, "Stronger for what, exactly?" What in the world do I need such immense strength and resilience for? This statement is neither comforting nor helpful. You will eventually find ways to handle and navigate these unhelpful and annoying comments. Even if it were true that this experience will make you stronger, it is difficult to look on the bright side when you are in the thick of things, just trying to get through your day and hoping that you will survive it all.

Yes, I know these comments are well-intentioned. I get that. I really do. However, once I have heard them for the 957th time, I start to get antsy. Thankfully, time and a sense of humour have softened my reactions. Now when I hear these comments, I just grin and shake my head, and the frustration subsides. It becomes funny after a while. You will see. One day, you will tell them between snorts of laughter that their simple maxims are complete bullshit.

Another thing you'll notice is people staring at you and your child when you're out. Let's be honest, we are programmed as humans to take a peek, have a gawk, be a looky-loo, even when we should mind our own business. We are naturally curious about anything different or unfamiliar that catches our eye. Most of us have learned or have been taught that staring is impolite. We might take a casual peek at something or someone and be equally casual when we look away. You know what I'm talking about: pretending that you are looking at something other than that lady's wild hairdo or that man's far-too-skimpy cut-off shorts! I have done it and I am sure you have, too.

What if (a) you were never taught that staring uncontrollably was rude, or (b) you never learned the art of staring discreetly? What if your desire to have a good gawk surpassed your built-in barometer of politeness and, well, you got distracted in your staring and got caught in the act? When a person does get caught, they either smile as though they weren't staring, glance around intensely, or abruptly look away in embarrassment. Some just keep on staring, even after the subject of their stare has made eye contact.

When I saw people watching Meredith, I used to chalk it up to normal human curiosity. She is different in a lot of ways and she is a prime target for curious onlookers. She is also cute. Why would people not look at her for her cuteness as well? My father, for one, gets very excited when he sees another child who resembles Meredith. We live in a town of 1,100 people. The only people here using wheelchairs are over 80, except for Meredith. My dad doesn't want to appear to be staring, but it is wonderful for him to see other children with CP. I have to assume that sometimes, the people who are watching us are doing so because we remind them of someone they know.

One of our family relief workers (FRWs) is very protective of Meredith. If anyone so much as glances at her, even smiling, she will give them a glare that says loud and clear and with unspoken words, "Quit gawking!!" Once, we were sitting in the waiting room at the ER and a woman was staring at us from across the room over the top of the novel she was reading. I mean, really staring. I was busy chatting about a movie I had seen the night before. Meredith was arching away, due to spasticity caused by the cerebral palsy, and I was moving right along with her, completely oblivious to this woman's eyeballing. Suddenly, our FRW raised her voice and shouted across the waiting room, "Why don't you take a picture?" Caught in the act, the woman sank into her chair and attempted to hide behind her romance paperback, but with little success. I think I had more empathy for her than the FRW did. I felt like following up her question with, "It's okay. I know she is interesting to look at."

I have accepted that people are going to stare and, for the most part, I am okay with it. I dealt with three children who stood on their front lawn and never broke their stare from the time they saw us coming up the street until we passed. This happened each time we were out on our morning walk. Finally, I looked at them and said, "Quit staring! It's rude!" I just got fed up with the fact that even though I smiled each time as we passed and said, "Good morning," they just stood there looking like creepy zombie children, staring us down as though we were from another planet.

Sometimes, these curious looks are an opportunity to engage with and educate others. At other times, I think people are forgetting their manners and need to be reminded. It depends on the situation, as well as on how much sleep I had the night before. If you have a child with extra needs, you may find that people take a peek more often than they normally would. Assume they are simply curious and, if you get the chance, strike up a conversation so that they can readily see that you are a regular parent – a parent like any other, with a child who appears a little more interesting than most.

Unless you plan to stay indoors for the rest of your child's life, you will be forced to deal with the masses. When our children are babies, it can be easier, because they often blend in with everyone else's babies. It can also be harder, though, because we are new at this whole parenting thing and can be overwhelmed simply having a new baby, whether or not this baby is our first. As they get older, it becomes easier because you will have developed a thicker skin.

What is even trickier than dealing with the general population is discovering that your own family members are having some comfort issues around this new family member. They may feel a sense of awkwardness around you and your child. You may notice that some of your family members and friends stop coming over as often. It has nothing to do with you or your child. It has everything to do with them. Having a child with extra needs comes as a bit of a shock not only to the child's immediate family, but also to friends, the extended family and the community. If your parents are among the ones having trouble, it helps to realize that they are likely not only heartbroken about their grandchild, they are also heartbroken for you and perhaps for your spouse.

It's tough dealing with the complicated feelings naturally stirred up when this type of thing happens. Sometimes (in fact, a lot of the time), people choose consciously or subconsciously to withdraw from their feelings. The unfortunate thing about burying our feelings is that they will find a way to surface one way or another. Oftentimes, sudden blow-ups with others have little to do with the topic at hand. More often than not, they have to do with things that have remained unspoken. It is easier for most of us to shut down and tune out than it is to be honest and, therefore, vulnerable.

If you feel that those close to you are tiptoeing around the proverbial elephant in the room, try to speak with them or suggest that they find some support. The agencies that help the families of children with extra needs often provide services for other family members. Most importantly, trust that, for the most part, the feelings and reactions of others have little, if anything, to do with you personally.

When Meredith was born, our two families coped in different ways. We respected both ways and tried to lead by example. We spoke openly about our struggles. Some family members couldn't bear to hear the real truth of our reality, while others shared how upsetting the situation was to them. Both responses challenged us. Over time, we learned to set guidelines and bound-aries for what we would handle and what they could handle themselves.

I lost friends after Meredith's birth because they were uncomfortable. Over the years, I made new friends who proved more loyal and accepting than those I'd left behind. It's not your job to make people comfortable with what life has presented you. Briefly acknowledge the loss of certain people in your life and then send them on their way knowing they no longer provide what you need in a friendship. As you evolve, you will attract more and more people who don't require such maintenance.

Over time, you will develop a keen sense of who deserves your energy and time and who does not. The masses will always be there. That doesn't change. You will, however, become an expert at conserving and managing your time and sharing it only with those who recognize its value.

CHAPTER 12

Everything Happens for a Reason?

Many people exclaim that "everything happens for a reason." I believe that we do more harm than good when we say this to someone struggling with whatever devastating blow has come their way. In my experience, reducing a difficult, shocking time to a "reason" is infuriating. Who wants to hear that there is some magical reason for what happened? How could I be comforted by the suggestion that our daughter's abrupt hypoxia, which completely ended the life she could have lived, had a purpose or a reason? It has never, ever brought me comfort.

To be clear, many years after Meredith's birth, I eventually made it to a place where I was able to accept what happened. Acceptance doesn't mean that I welcomed what happened, or saw it as a "gift." I didn't. There will always be a deep-seated sadness about the fact that we will never experience normal parenting and that Meredith was robbed of a normal childhood and life. Being a mother to Meredith has changed me in ways that I never could have anticipated. But I would argue that this was not the reason she was dealt a brain injury. I am where I am today because of the choices I have made along the way.

These "reason" statements angered me at first. Part of me felt that I needed to grasp this truth and believe it. I figured that since most people were proclaiming this as "the truth," it must therefore be true. I might be in the middle of describing our daily struggles, punctuated by sudden emergencies, including frantic calls to 911 or ambulance rides to the emergency room, when whomever I was speaking to would smile and say, "Well, I guess everything happens for a reason." By the time we were ten years into our parenting challenges, I was simply tired and bored with this kind of rationalization.

I recognize that for many people the belief that everything happens for a reason is comforting and takes the onus off of them. When people say this to me, they assume that (a) we share similar (religious) beliefs or that (b) by minimizing what I am going through (with such a broad statement about the workings of the universe), I might be comforted. Both assumptions are inaccurate.

The problem with the belief that everything happens for a reason is that it makes us feel powerless. Between birth and death is a vast collection of experiences – extraordinary experiences that we will perceive as either good or bad. The experiences themselves, in their raw form, do not define our evolution as a person. What we do with those experiences makes the difference. Ten people can be dealing with the exact same situation and circumstance, yet each one will perceive and move through that experience in their own way. It isn't actually what happens, but rather what you happen to do with it that will define the situation. We have the power to create something meaningful from all of our experiences.

I have come to realize that the deeper the despair we transcend, the greater the lessons we learn. But going through hardships, gaining insight and achieving self-growth are not enough. We must be willing to share what we have learned and gained on our journeys. For those of us who are parents of children with medical fragility, the journey is ongoing. There is a definite beginning with an unknown end. We emerge periodically from the dark, dense forest into sunny clearings where we regroup, catch our breath and are reminded that there is always light after darkness or in the midst of darkness. Always.

Willingness. Letting go. Acceptance. These words can make a difference between finding joy and living in despair. It can be both as complicated and as simple as that. The moment we heard the prognosis of Meredith's brain injury, a switch flipped inside my brain, and I verbally affirmed that we would be okay. Just hours into this journey, however, I began to question whether or not we would actually be okay. Since then, my husband and I have encountered metaphorical dragons much more fierce and vicious than we ever could have imagined.

For me back then, "being okay" meant leading a relatively normal life where we could still carry on with activities that brought happiness and joy. I also occasionally questioned whether my husband and I had the stamina to both individually and collectively survive the extreme unrelenting stress we found ourselves living with on a daily basis. Those early years involved severe, ongoing sleep deprivation, raw grief and a learning curve so steep that I often found myself losing my grip and tumbling backwards. Then I had to start all over again.

We cannot change what has happened to us. As much as we thrash about and scream and cry, we are still going to find ourselves in the same circumstances (in our case, as parents of a child with medical fragility and other complexities). The only control you have in that moment is to make the choice of taking on the challenge and emerging triumphant – albeit battered and worn, but triumphant nonetheless – with a wealth of wisdom and teachings to share with those who need it.

CHAPTER 13

Isolation

A new parent's enemy is isolation. When Meredith was born, she spent ten weeks in the NICU and, although there were other babies and parents, it was still isolating. We were asked to respect each other's privacy, and most of us weren't feeling very social anyway.

When we were fortunate, we would get into the parent room (a.k.a. "the cuddle room"), a space where we could shut ourselves away from everyone else, including the staff, and exhale. On other days we surrounded ourselves with makeshift walls, cloth partitions that separated us from other parents and their babies, to create a private space.

I used to encourage expectant parents in my prenatal classes to stay in touch and plan to get together with their fellow prenatal classmates. This connection with other new parents is critical, especially for the health and well-being of the primary care parent. In fact, the hormonal system of the new mother is set up to crave company in those early postpartum days and weeks. When the normal pattern of things has been disrupted by an emergency caesarean birth or other intervention, this hormonal cocktail is interrupted. It has been demonstrated that some new mothers do not intuitively seek out or desire the company of other mothers. This results in further isolation, leaving them at greater risk for postpartum adjustment problems and stress.

When I became a new mother, I intuitively felt the need to connect with other mothers whose children were even remotely similar to Meredith. At the time, I was unaware that there would be so few parents with children like Meredith. We were also unclear about the seriousness of her brain damage. We knew the diagnosis was severe cerebral palsy, so I sought parents of children with similar diagnoses. I knew that I had to connect with parents whose children had unexpectedly been born with a brain injury and medical fragility.

I connected with a Vancouver woman who had a 14-year-old daughter with cerebral palsy. She was the cousin of a friend, and the first person with whom I had communicated about being a mother of a child with extra needs. Exchanging emails with this mother who was further down this path helped me feel less isolated.

In one of her emails, she casually mentioned that her husband was out for a run, not realizing the weight of her words. This one statement gave me incredible hope. She went on to mention that they were planning a weekend away to Whistler, and I remember thinking specifically in that moment, "Oh my gosh, there is hope for us! We, too, might someday be able to go away like normal parents."

The hospital social worker made it clear to us that she could not give out information about other parents, which was understandable. We begged her to give our names and number to other families, other new parents who were experiencing a similar reality. We wanted to connect with others who shared similar struggles. No connections were ever made at the hospital, and it was quite a long time before I felt that I had found my "tribe," people I had so much in common with.

My first tribe was a group of women from across the globe that I had met through an online forum. We posted questions and comments in hopes that someone somewhere would lovingly nod their virtual head in recognition. Still, I felt isolated. While I knew they were all real people living somewhat similar circumstances, we could only connect online.

It wasn't until November 2010, when Meredith was turning seven and was in hospital for double hip surgery, that we made our first in-person connection with another family whose story reflected our own. Their son was to undergo gastrostomy tube (G-tube) surgery, which places a tube into the stomach for feeding. Our daughter and their son ended up sharing a room on the ward. We could hear the little boy through the curtain that divided us, and he sure sounded like Meredith. Later that evening, the boy's father popped his head around the corner and said, "It sounds like you have a similar model." That was the beginning of a friendship, not only between us, but also between Meredith and their son, who had a similar outcome from his own birth. They also led me to my next tribe.

Upon their urging, I joined a support group through the palliative care home that our children were both referred to. I didn't attend my first group until the spring of 2011. I was hesitant to go. I felt I was managing and didn't need to sit around with a group of people feeling sorry for themselves, but in the end I gave it a try. It was far more rewarding than I had ever expected. It was a relief to be in the same room with other parents who understood what I was going through each day.

It is critical for all parents to have their own tribe, especially when living with the reality that our child is likely to die before we do. This group of people soon became our lifeline. They are the ones who really and truly get it. They understand the depth and the essence of the exhaustion, stress, challenges and all the conflicting emotions that we feel from time to time while walking this path.

My tribe is diverse. We all deal with different challenges, come from different backgrounds, and are at different stages in our lives. When we meet each month, I can relax and breathe and say whatever is on my mind. Sometimes, our raw, unedited and clear-cut way of expressing ourselves shocks our social workers, but we know that our group is a safe place where we can be real and not be judged.

Wherever you are on this journey, whatever your situation, I cannot stress enough how important it is for you to find your tribe, your hive, your clan, your hub, your group, your people. We cannot take this journey on our own. I suppose we *could*, but isolation would make it much more difficult. The fact remains that the parents of neuro-typical, healthy children can empathize, but they can never really understand.

If your community is found only online because there are no families that resemble yours in your neighbourhood or if you're not blessed to have a palliative care home in your vicinity or some kind of suitable parent support group, that's okay. There are many of us out there. Our numbers are growing, and we need each other.

I suspect and hope that today's new parents do not experience the extreme isolation that parents like us, who gave birth before the social media era kicked in, did. In 2015, I was invited to join a Facebook group for parents with children who experienced hypoxia at birth. I am constantly amazed at the remarkable level of support, coupled with the words of love and encouragement exchanged each day. Mothers and fathers who are a mere six weeks postpartum share their stories and are met with comments letting them know that they are not alone and that, although they've ended up on a rough road, it will get easier. As a result of joining this group, my tribe has grown immensely.

Ideally, it's best to also connect offline with at least one other parent travelling a similar path. There is a deeper level of connection that is achieved when you can physically share space with others. We only see a portion of each other online. The opportunity to meet with others and be in the presence of their feelings, trials and triumphs is one that should not be missed.

Other than my spouse, the members of my tribe are truly the only other people on this planet who can empathize with me and understand my day-to-day life, even though our experiences differ. No one quite understands the complexities and the layers of ongoing stress that are part of parenting a child with multiple needs and fragility like ours.

When I am with my tribe, I usually get a good idea of how my head and heart are doing. During these two hours set aside for our face-to-face interaction, I can avoid all distractions, including the multitude of tasks that must be fulfilled each day. Meeting with my tribe involves driving more than 200 kilometres (124 miles) round-trip, and many times I can barely muster the effort to get there. But I have learned over time that it is a necessity for my health. These sessions never disappoint, and I feel rejuvenated afterward.

Oftentimes, it is during the initial check-in, when we update other group members and introduce ourselves to newcomers, that I realize I have neglected my emotional health. My tears start to flow, and the mother sitting beside me recognizes those tears. As I look up through blurry eyes, I see the faces of weary, warrior parents staring back at me. And although their eyes are tired, they look at me with understanding. No one has to say a word.

I am not expecting words of comfort anyway. A box of tissues is passed towards me, and I am left to express the deepest emotions attached to the tears that fall and to reflect on what we might be going through at that time with our daughter.

In the last couple of years, I have sometimes gone months without attending my parent group. Things had been relatively stable with Meredith, and so I didn't need the support as I did in the early days. Recently, though, Meredith's health status is changing and I have returned to attending group once again. I realize that even when I may not be in need, I can provide a listening ear and some words of wisdom to those who are in the beginning years of parenting. It takes courage and confidence and a big leap of faith to expose yourself and find your tribe. It is necessary for your survival. You need your tribe as much as you need food, water and air.

CHAPTER 14

Working with Professionals

When raising a child with extra needs, you become part of a larger circle of support than most parents. You are dealing with medical personnel (doctors, nurses and specialists), therapists in a variety of areas (physiotherapy, occupational therapy, speech/language, infant development) and government agencies that fund and provide assistance with equipment. In addition to the government-run agencies, there are organizations set up to support families like ours, such as Easter Seals, United Cerebral Palsy and March of Dimes, to name a few. Depending on the degree of extra needs your child has, you may also have regular family relief workers and/or nurses spending time in your home on a daily or nightly basis.

For the most part, you will find people who choose this field of work to be genuinely kind and caring people who have a passion for working with children like ours. You may feel a sense of relief when you learn that you will not be alone on this journey. There will be "tour guides" along the way to assist you, provide you with information and direct you to where you need to go. It can be overwhelming to know that, for the rest of your child's life, you will share your child's care with a team of experts. They provide relief or frustration, depending on your state of mind on any particular day.

One of the most challenging aspects of becoming a parent to Meredith was the number of people who suddenly became part of our lives. Tim and I are fairly private people, so to have social workers, discharge planners, case managers, and developmental services coordinators, among others, calling and setting up meetings and appointments on a daily basis produced a lot of anxiety, to say the least.

When we are at our best, we can respond to stress effectively. Following a birth, sleep deprivation and high stress levels make us feel less able to manage. It can be extremely difficult to ask professionals the questions that need to be asked and to tell them how we feel. We may use protective responses that give the impression that we are "fine and okay" and "handling it all" because, somewhere beyond the strong persona we present to the world, there is a terrified parent who fears that any sign of weakness or lack of confidence suggests that we are incapable of caring for our child. It can be frightening to have so many individuals involved in such a personal experience.

Still, we need reassurance because we are dealing with more than we anticipated. You will find the majority of professionals you come in contact with to be kind people. Some will be more like counsellors to you, especially in the beginning when you are desperately trying to figure it all out. Your infant development worker may come to visit your baby and, instead, spend the entire hour listening to your worries and concerns. This can be invaluable. You will grow your confidence faster if the professionals who are supposed to help you with your baby or child are aware that you too may need extra care at times. Because this is not part of their job description, you will learn to identify those whom you can confide in and who can provide reassurance on a regular basis.

It is critical that you be honest with the professionals in your life. While it can be tempting to sugar-coat what is really going on with your child, you will do yourself and others a disservice if you are dishonest about your reality. They need to know, for example, that you are not sleeping because your child is sleepless. If you have gut feelings about any aspect of your child's well-being, you must tell them. Your intuition can be more valuable than any medical degree. It takes time to trust the accuracy of your intuition, but after you have ignored it several times and then regretted it, you will not care if your intuitive feelings come across as a little eccentric. I often preface my words with, "This might sound completely crazy but …" This lets the person I'm talking to know that I'm aware my "feeling" seems strange, even to me.

Eventually, the specialists involved in your life for many months and years will start to trust your "feeling" more than the assessment just performed by a new resident or medical student. If you spend any length of time in the hospital, at some point you will transition from receiving direction from professionals to finally feeling that YOU, and only you, are the parent. During the first ten weeks of Meredith's life in the hospital, I mostly felt that I was just along for the ride. There were so many people providing so much of the care that I didn't really know where my role as her mother belonged. There were several admissions to the hospital before I could stand firmly in my "mother boots" and feel that we were not only Meredith's parents, but also her primary caregivers and decision-makers.

This relationship with professionals can be tricky and complex, depending on where you are on this path. I shudder to think of how challenging it must have been for the professionals who helped our family in those very early days and months. Only now can I appreciate their patience, their understanding and their wisdom in knowing when it was best to give us time alone. There were only a few professionals with whom we were incompatible, and we dealt with those quickly. For the most part we have been extremely fortunate, and we never lose sight of the gift most of them have been to our family. We are profoundly aware that we would never have been able to care for Meredith at home without the behind-the-scenes work and care so many people provided. Clear expectations, honesty and a willingness to bend a little: these are the qualities I believe are needed to adjust to the many professionals who will inevitably become a part of your life from now on.

What I would tell you
. . . about the emotional realities

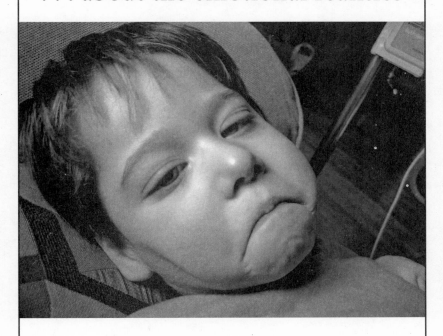

CHAPTER 15

Emotional Excavating

W hen I was twenty or so, I read the book *Women's Bodies: Women's Wisdom* by Dr. Christiane Northrup. It not only confirmed many of the things I had entertained about the body/mind connection, it also introduced the concepts of true healing and real health. It demonstrated that healing was far more complex than simply treating symptoms.

For those of us who have endured years of unimaginable emotional experiences (initial shock of being told your child has a brain injury or a genetic disorder, or near-death episodes, or the daily and nightly grind of caregiving, to name a few), there is usually little time to process and express all the ups and downs of our life with our child with extra needs. On top of that, especially after months and years have passed, it seems nearly impossible to muster the courage and desire to even "go there."

But what happens when we do not revisit these emotions and give them the expression they require? They can make our muscles tight and stiff. They can cause restriction in our diaphragm, making it difficult to breathe. They can be the culprit behind low back pain, panic attacks, headaches and insomnia. They can come out in spurts in the form of outbursts of anger or overreactions to things. They can ooze into our relationships with our spouses and wreak havoc in our marriages. If not tended to, they can easily, as a collective, morph into depression and/or anxiety. As scary as it is to think about, going "there" is exactly what one must do to get unstuck.

So where is "there," exactly? I imagine that there is a holding tank within our bodies where unresolved, unexpressed and really difficult emotions reside. It is the place where all of those feelings sit and wait until we have the freedom and space and time to allow their expression. Conveniently enough, all of these tend to be in short supply for parents like us. When high levels of stress and extraordinary events (oftentimes traumatic) occur over and over again throughout a long period of time (months and even years), I think that this holding tank reaches its capacity and spills over. I imagine that when these emotions spill over, they creep into any other spaces within the body available for storage. This may be one of the variables involved in chronic pain and muscle tension.

One thing to keep in mind is that you have already lived through the experience that's attached to these repressed emotions and memories. In some ways, as you remember and release the feelings, it may feel as though you are re-living the experience, but you will never have to go through it in real time again. Sometimes our anticipatory fear gets in our way. What if we tap into those tears and then we can't stop crying? What if that anger is so powerful we lose control of ourselves? What if I actually face those feelings of grief – does it mean I don't love my child?

The key is to move through these thoughts. They are there to protect you from the really hard emotions, and they are the reason you have managed to keep your feelings down for so long. But in the long run they are not serving you well. A time will come when you will have to go "there." When that time comes, there are resources available to assist you in the process (see Chapter 8 on Self-Care).

If you are not yet at a place where you want to go "there" in the form of emotional spelunking, simply give yourself ten minutes of alone time per day where you lie down and breathe. Get comfortable, place your hand on your solar plexus (just beneath where your chest ends and your abdominal cavity begins between the ribs) and take slow breaths in through your nose and out through your mouth. Allow the tension to leave each limb. If you feel movement within and emotions start to arise, allow yourself these ten minutes to weep or to remember. This can easily happen once you give yourself the space. Move through your fear and give yourself this much-needed release.

Trust that you can put the lid on the proverbial container if you feel overwhelmed. You can be in control of how much you release at any given time. Sometimes our busy-ness and imagined lack of time are ways of avoiding the excavation. You do have ten minutes per day, though. Carve it out of the time you spend watching television or being on the Internet. Remember that these repressed emotions will not resolve on their own no matter how much time passes. Digging deep and unearthing them might be the best gift you can give yourself and your family.

CHAPTER 16

Relinquishing Control

In a nutshell, here's what I know about control: you don't have a whole lot of it. You likely have far less control than you think you have. You may play tricks on yourself by trying to find some sort of control, even though you know instinctively that it is all an illusion.

I was in a car accident three years before Meredith was born. I was stopped at a traffic light when I was hit from behind by a fishtailing Volvo. It wasn't a serious accident, but I was left with chronic pain, was unable to work and was forced to take legal action.

We tend to think that we are immune if we are doing things "right," and that these events happen to *other* people. But we are all hit with unexpected events, outcomes and tragedies; it happens every minute of every day all over the world. Intellectually, we know there are no guarantees. People say it all the time, whether you are going through the line-up at a wake or listening to the reflective sermon at a funeral. Some part of us believes that these terrible things can't possibly happen to us – until they do.

When life is unfair, we naturally blame someone or something for our misfortune. We need a place to unload our seething anger, frustration and despair. Sometimes, there is a legitimate explanation for why these things happen. Perhaps your doctor or midwife made a medical error or a bad call. Maybe your child choked on that sandwich, which resulted in a lack of oxygen and then brain damage, because the daycare provider was chatting on the phone. Maybe your neighbour would have seen your ten-year-old on his bike and not hit him, had he been paying attention.

When we cannot find someone or something to blame, we tend to blame ourselves. Our mind starts to replay every detail preceding the event: "I was unknowingly pregnant when I attended that St. Patrick's Day party and drank all night." "Maybe I shouldn't have eaten that fast food when I was seven months pregnant." "I was foolish to go with a midwife; I should have just scheduled a caesarean." "I should have listened to my friends who told me that my obstetrician was too quick to intervene." "Maybe if I had given birth vaginally this wouldn't have happened."

Welcome to one of the darkest places your mind will travel to. It is a long road with no destination. The truth of the matter is that you are likely never going to know what happened and, even if you do or think you do, it will never change the outcome. What has happened has happened. This is it, and it is one hard pill to swallow.

This idea of "coming to terms with everything" is a process. It can take time, and you will need breaks. Personally, I went first to the strange land of denial. I put on my professional doula hat and defended our decisions and our midwife as though my life depended on it. We made an educated and informed decision to have a home birth with one of the best midwives on the continent. We had to deal with an onslaught of ignorant comments from professionals and family members alike. People suggested that, if Meredith had been born in the hospital, the outcome would have been different. Others asked if I would plan a caesarean birth next time, or if perhaps our tragedy occurred because home births don't use the same medical equipment as hospitals. I had attended enough births as a doula to know with certainty that what happened at our birth would have unfolded the same way had we been in the hospital. I fully recognized that, no matter what we do, things unfold as they will.

There was a part of me that believed that, if you ate the right food, read the right books, chose the right care provider, had all of the right supports in place and basically did everything right, you were pretty much guaranteed that all would be well. I was shocked to learn that this is not the case.

When you first realize that you do not have complete control, this can cause suffocating anxiety. The sense of control is nothing but an illusion. The irony is that the moment you absorb this knowledge fully and transform it into a belief, you will feel a sense of peace and calm. It is a relief to recognize and know that you do not have control.

Of course, you do have control over some things. You have control over how you will react and over the actions you will take from that point forward. Your reality will be a whole lot easier to cope with if you take steps to relinquish the things you cannot control.

The very act of scrambling to control what is unfolding right before your eyes is very disempowering. It gives you a false sense of security and, in the end, it will leave you awake at night, worrying in the darkness about all of the possible, imagined outcomes. You may feel that you can't help worrying. Worry is a natural reaction when you are presented with abnormal circumstances. The key is to let worry wash over you and then let it go. When your stress and anxiety levels are high, your mind will start to run frantically like a hamster on a wheel. This immense feeling of anxiety is both terrifying and exhausting. Your attempts to control situations and circumstances only lead to increased anxiety because, for the most part, you cannot control the outcome. One of the simplest and most powerful actions you can take on this journey is to surrender and trust that the answers you need will come to you.

The moment I find myself beginning to fret, I simply take stock of everything that Tim and I have endured over the last 14 years. In a deep part of myself, I know that, one way or another, we will get through whatever crisis may come. Surrender isn't easy. Getting through the challenging periods will still take your breath away, but your energy will go into coping with what is real, as opposed to running from what may or may not happen.

CHAPTER 17

The Burden of Guilt

I assume that mothers, since the beginning of time, have always experienced what is known as "mother guilt." Fathers definitely experience this as well, though perhaps not to the extent mothers do. Fathers may feel less guilt, due to biology or emotional make-up, or the simple fact that, in the majority of cases, the mother is the primary caregiver. Nevertheless, the mother guilt that I refer to in this chapter can be applied to fathers as well.

When I discussed new parenthood in my prenatal classes, I spent some time talking about how guilt tends to seep in and make the experience of parenting more challenging than it needs to be. If I asked a group of expectant parents if they had ever heard the term "mother guilt," they usually shook their heads and looked at me wide-eyed for clarification. If I asked the same question to a group of seasoned mothers, though, I was met with nods, loud sighs and "uh-huhs" echoing throughout the room. They would look at one another with knowing smiles as if to say, "Yep, we know all about that."

For some, pregnancy triggers a downward spiral into a muddy puddle of guilt. If our blood pressure rises, we feel guilty that we might be hurting our baby. If we go for a long walk and suddenly experience mild contractions, we feel guilty for almost putting ourselves into labour. If our babies are not growing fast enough, or if they are too big, we ask ourselves how we could have prevented these situations.

Labour and birth set the stage for an onslaught of fresh guilt feelings, especially for those experiencing an unexpected outcome. A mother who planned a natural birth but ends up requiring medications and possibly a caesarean may feel guilty about the impact the birth could have on her baby. Mothers who bottle-feed their children, whether by choice or by necessity, may feel a sense of guilt and berate themselves with thoughts such as "Maybe I didn't try hard enough." Guilt sets in as they read the plethora of information regarding breastfeeding versus bottle-feeding.

Parents of healthy children may experience guilt if their child becomes sick or has an accident, believing that if they'd taken better care of their child, they could have prevented the virus or the fall.

Then there are parents like me who give birth to children who have a genetic condition, had a brain injury due to a traumatic birth, or were born seemingly healthy but developed some rare disorder in their first few months or years of life. This experience of parenting can take guilt to a whole new level.

We are complex parents because we are caring for complex children. We deal with complicated emotions and thought processes. Having negative thoughts, or negative reactions to events, is not the problem. The problem, I believe, is that parents get caught up in the guilt that might follow. We daydream about getting away, really getting away – jumping in the car and heading straight for Mexico and not looking back. This fleeting thought is quickly followed by guilt.

We wonder what life would be like if our child had been born healthy. Suddenly we are struck by guilt. How could we think such a thing? This child is perfect as she is, how could we dare to think otherwise? We watch our child suffer. We watch our child teeter on the brink of death. A small part of us begs the universe to just take our child and end this roller coaster ride. Then bang! Feelings of guilt slam into us the moment such a thought crosses our mind. And some days we are just bone-tired of being a parent that needs to give so much all the time. Our inability to be at peace as real-life Florence Nightingales leaves us riddled with feelings of guilt.

Guilt is all about feeling like you did something wrong. When you begin to feel guilty, ask yourself if there was negative intention behind your thought or action. For example, if your child gets a urinary tract infection for perhaps the ninth time in a year, you may be overwhelmed with guilt once again. You wonder if you failed to provide sufficient hygiene, or if you selected the wrong soap or laundry detergent or diapers.

If these thoughts start to roll in, stop for a moment and ask yourself: "Did I intentionally cause my child to get the urinary tract infection?" I'm going to go out on a limb here, but I bet your answer would be "no." Follow this question with: "Am I doing the best I can with the knowledge I have?" I would estimate that 99.99 per cent of the time the answer to this question would be "yes."

There is so much that we cannot control. Feeling guilty for things you did not intend to happen or over which you have absolutely no control wastes your precious energy, the very energy you need to care for your child.

If you are a guilt addict, you may feel guilty now about feeling guilty. Stop. Give yourself a break. You are doing the best you can with the resources, knowledge and means at your disposal. That is enough. Proceed with love and good intention and say farewell to guilt. There is no space in your life for it. And what if you do have thoughts about heading for the border? My advice is to be gentle with yourself. Your mind is simply finding a way to express how truly desperate you feel at times. A little daydreaming can be helpful.

Guilt is tricky and can be very subtle. You may not even identify it as "guilt," but it is always a form of self-punishment. Guilt requires an awful lot of energy, and it will get you nowhere.

There may be times when guilt is warranted. If you have made a bad choice or committed a wrongdoing, for example, admit to it and then take steps to resolve it. Being proactive will prevent you from becoming stuck in the quicksand of guilt.

The problem with guilt is that it gives us permission to remain passive, as though everything is out of our control. We can say, "I just feel so guilty for losing my cool with my child, but she is so demanding. I just can't handle it." Rather than apologizing to your child for losing patience only to repeat the behaviour, figure out what you can change to better cope with the demands of caring for your child.

The next step would be to share your feelings with someone else, be it your partner, another parent, a trusted friend or a family member. Share that you are unhappy with your behaviour, then work together on a solution. It may be that you need more sleep, that you have to adjust your schedule so that you are not spread too thin, or that you need to ask for more help.

Ridding yourself of guilt is possible. If your guilt comes from something you control, such as your behaviour, then acknowledge it and find solutions to correct the behaviour. On the other hand, if the guilt you feel comes from something over which you have no control, such as your child's inheriting a genetic disorder from you, or you accidentally yanking their feeding tube out of their stomach, the cure is simple but powerful. You start by showing yourself love and compassion.

So many of our judgments stem from the messages we received throughout our lives. When you think, "I am such a bad mother," stop yourself and think about the facts supporting this statement about yourself. Are you really a bad mother? You did not intentionally ask for your child to have a genetic disorder, nor did you intend to cause injury to your child. Counteract these thoughts with loving thoughts. After an accident, tell yourself, "It was an accident. I made a mistake. I forgive myself, as I would anyone else." Be as respectful, caring and gentle with yourself as you would be with your child, a friend or a stranger if they were beating themselves up unnecessarily.

We are flawed and imperfect human beings bumbling along this path of life. All of us are doing the best we can. Contrary to popular belief, some days we do get more than we can handle. Begin by learning to love yourself a little bit more each day. Eventually, the toxic feelings of guilt will dissipate, and you will feel lighter, empowered and more in control of your actions and your life. Feeling badly about something we have done is simply a red flag telling us that an adjustment needs to be made. Feeling guilty about what we have no control over tells us that we need to start loving ourselves a little more.

CHAPTER 18

Enough is Enough

I have been trotting on this path long enough to know that guilt will suck the life force out of you faster than anything. Keeping this in mind, I tend not to spend time in a pit of guilt when it comes to our beautifully complex daughter. However, every so often, there is one question that still finds its way to my conscious mind.

Out of nowhere, I am plagued with this:

DID WE DO ENOUGH FOR HER???

The question cements itself there in my mind. It stays there until I finish having the same logical conversation with myself I've been having for years to soothe the worry, regret, fear, and yes, guilt that accompanies it.

We are 14 years into this and still, although very rarely now, I wonder, "Did we do enough for her?" I am not talking about her medical or practical care. I am confident in the care we have given her and know that without it, she wouldn't be alive today. I am talking more about the things I see online that people have tried and had success with. I am talking about therapies that could have changed the course of her life.

I read about the great lengths parents have gone to in order for their child to receive specialized therapies – travelling across the county or even across the world to access these therapies. New parents write about their child's diagnosis with the vocabulary and medical knowledge of someone with a doctorate in neurology. As I read how other parents share all the details of their child's diagnosis, the online world has made my shortcomings glaringly apparent. There are levels of HIE, I find out now? Ask me what our daughter's level is and I couldn't tell you. All that's etched in my mind is: *"Hypoxic Ischemic Encephalopathy resulting in severe, life-limiting cerebral palsy."* The day Hypoxic Ischemic Encephalopathy rolled off my tongue was a big day for me!

In the beginning of our parenting experience, social media did not exist as it does now. I combed the library at the children's hospital only to find outdated books about raising your child with cerebral palsy. The illustrations were of kids, who looked happy enough, tossing a football around from their wheelchair with their school pals. I thought to myself: "This isn't so bad."

Then I found a dusty book in a second-hand store called *What To Do About Your Brain-Injured Child* (1974 edition). I thought I had struck gold, and was determined to do everything in my power for this story to have a happy ending. I imagined reading it cover to cover and then applying my new knowledge with Meredith. I imagined the doctor's faces when one day she WALKED into her neurologist's office (thanks to the therapies I had researched and applied). That fantasy was obliterated when reality slammed into it like a freight train. How was I going to read this book and get my honourary neurology degree when I had to stop and start feeds around the clock every 1.5 hours, plus deal with pumping breast milk every three hours? How was I to do the daily hours of therapy when we had to hold our new baby 15 hours per day? Then there were the retching episodes, seizures, baths, dressing changes, medications, doctor's appointments, and severe lack of sleep. It became clear, very quickly, that I was not going to be reading that book anytime soon.

There was no shortage of well-meaning friends and family doing "research" for us and sending scientific papers on all kinds of things we could do to "fix" our daughter. As the ideas for therapies and even some magical cures rolled in, I felt my resilience weaken as I tried to comprehend how we could logistically and financially give her the best shot at improving her status.

At one point, a kind nurse practitioner drove us to Ottawa (120 kilometres away) to check out a hyperbaric oxygen tank. Travelling any distance with Meredith was nothing short of a nightmare, but we were willing to investigate anything that might help. This therapy would have involved lying in a claustrophobia-inducing tube with Meredith in my arms for an hour at a time. She choked and retched constantly, and she needed to move the way her disorganized brain demanded her to. There was no way this therapy would be an option (not to mention the thousands of dollars we'd need to come up with to pay for it). Then it was onto Conductive Education, which we were gently told probably wasn't going to be doable for our severely affected daughter.

Throughout all of this we were giving therapies in our home and receiving regular visits from an occupational therapist and a physiotherapist, as well as seating and communication experts. Through the years we tried conventional therapies along with many unconventional modalities: chiropractic, massage therapy, craniosacral therapy, osteopathy, naturopathy, homeopathy, functional medicine, Snowdrop therapy, essential oils. We even stretched ourselves out of our comfort zone by trying things like holy water from Mount St. Patrick, energy work, prayer circles from a distance, and soul retrieval (not even kidding!).

It wasn't until we decided to try out Snowdrop, which originates from the UK, that we had our reality handed back to us on a silver platter. The kind and knowledgeable neurologist who designed this therapy reviewed Meredith's MRI and assessed the countless videos and questionnaires we'd prepared. He concluded that it was very unlikely these therapies would do a whole lot. He wasn't dismal, but he was realistic. He did offer a bit of hope, saying, "It never hurts to try." And so we paid the hundreds of dollars and received the therapy program laid out for Meredith. We were diligent; performing the tasks every single day, four times a day for weeks, which turned into months. There was a teeny tiny bit of progress, and to us that made it all worth it. Eventually, we recognized that she had plateaued. The reality that our girl was likely going to stay comfortably at the zero-to-three-months level of development became blatantly obvious.

It is normal for new parents to scour the world for some therapy or treatment that will improve their child's abilities and life. I think of it as one of many "developmental" stages in parenting a child with extra needs. We must be cautious that we do not forget about living with our child and enjoying them just the way they are, in our quest to change the outcome.

There will be things that work, and there may be many things that do not. Sometimes you will have energy and motivation to spend hours each day applying specialized therapies. Other times you will be too exhausted to have a shower, and the therapies won't be high on your list of priorities. Does this make you a bad, lazy parent? Not in my books, it doesn't.

But how can you not feel as though you're coming up short when everyone else seems to be handling this remarkably well and, not only that, their kids have beaten the odds? Maybe if we did more, researched more, held them more, held them less, flew to Romania for two years for therapy, bought that goat and milked it to make our own formula, spent the hundreds of dollars on that treatment, things would be different.

This is what I have realized: we did the very best we could with what we had and what we were capable of doing at any given time. Someone else might have had great success in Romania, but we know this option was not feasible for us. We wish things would have been different; maybe if her brain was just a little less affected, we could have flown to another country to seek specialized therapies or I could have crammed my body and hers into a hyperbaric oxygen tank. But that wasn't our reality (and still isn't). To be honest, even if we could have afforded it and managed to get there, I am not sure we would have. At some point, we needed to face the reality that no matter what, our daughter would always be severely affected.

Does that mean we gave up on her? Absolutely not. It just meant that we recognized our limitations and made a conscious decision to stop comparing our situation to what everyone else was going through. We chose to feel secure in our decisions, and in the fact that we were doing everything possible to help her along to the degree that worked for her and for us.

Honestly, there was a big part of us that wanted to simply spend every moment enjoying her, knowing that our time with her was, like everything else, very limited. It didn't make sense to put her through forty hours per week of intensive therapy only to have very little improvement. For some families this brings tremendous results, but for families like ours, not so much. Eventually, you come to accept that no amount of prayer, magical chanting, love, determination and belief will change the outcome or beat the odds. It is an illusion that if we just love enough, believe enough, pray enough and do enough, our child will achieve all the things the doctors said they never would. If this were the case, I guarantee, our daughter would be training for the Olympics.

Believing that our child's outcome is a direct result of the level of love, care, therapy and magic we infused into their lives can leave us shattered and guilt-ridden if the outcome is not how we'd imagined it to be. On the flip side, if our child has soared above all expectations, and we tell others that with enough love and determination their child, too, can beat the odds, we (unintentionally) fertilize their feelings of guilt.

So how do you get from the place of feeling like you aren't doing enough to a place of accepting that you *are* doing enough? It's a process. It's learning to build on your child's strengths as opposed to trying to "fix" them or make them "normal." It comes from making the shift from putting your focus on the negative (what your child can't do) to the positive (what your child can do). It comes from examining your own feelings, challenging your beliefs, saying "NO" to guilt, trusting that you *are* doing the best you can with what you have in this moment.

And that is enough. Your child is enough, you are enough. Enough is enough.

CHAPTER 19

Befriending Grief

One of the most complex emotions that humans experience is grief. For me, grief is a soupy blend of deep sadness, despair, anger, frustration, pity, distress and depression, seasoned with regrets, what-ifs, denial, resentments and a sense of longing. I have never been a fan of grief and I kept it at bay for many years. I wore an extra-large cloak of resilience and stamina so that grief would not stand a chance. I was intellectually aware of the "losses" I had experienced, such as my dream of a healthy child, and getting the chance to mother and breastfeed my baby in the ways I had expected to. These are the obvious losses.

Then there are the less obvious ones: the micro-losses that took me by surprise. Little things such as seeing my step dancing shoes packed away in a box and realizing our daughter would never take dance lessons, or dance at all for that matter. Reminders surrounded me: pregnant women flush with anticipation for the birth of their child, new mothers walking around with their newborns snug against them in slings, mothers breastfeeding their babies with ease on a park bench or in a restaurant. When I received news that a family member or friend was pregnant, I would feel the tug of grief, yet put on a joyful face to avoid ruining the moment for them. The list seemed endless. There were reminders everywhere that we were on this road that was not of our choosing.

Grief comes like a sudden rain shower in the middle of a drought. The landscape is dry, the sunshine continuous, heat everywhere: you forget there was ever such a thing as rain, and assume that it will never return. You begin to adapt to drought, feeling confident that you can live without rain. And then you feel it: rain is on its way. You recognize the telltale signs. You catch a hint of its scent or feel a drop or two on your skin. You realize that you can no longer deny its existence as the wind picks up and the storm clouds move in. You shut everything down and settle in while the rainstorm moves through. It could destroy everything in its path, and yet after it has borne down on the dry and parched earth, there is relief. The sun breaks through again. That is how it is with grief.

When you feel the rumblings of old grief rise to the surface, you rationalize what else this feeling might be. It could be indigestion, exhaustion or perhaps the flu. But then, if you lie still with one hand on your solar plexus, your heart or your stomach, you feel the tears swell. There is no denying it or fighting it. It must wash over you like that sudden rainstorm. Sometimes it's like a steady gentle rain; other times, it's as though a hurricane warning is in effect. What has provoked this grief? It may be immediately obvious to you, or it may require some reflection.

One evening, eight and a half years after our daughter's birth, I visited my sister Stephanie's blog. Her latest post showed the ultrasound image of her fourth child, who was due one day before our daughter's birthday. It wasn't the ultrasound picture but the words accompanying the image that triggered my grief. She had typed out the lyrics to a song I heard for the first time when I was pregnant with Meredith. A client had given me a CD that included this song as a thank-you for attending the birth of their child. It became the theme song of my pregnancy, and the words are written out on the first page of Meredith's first baby book. When I scrolled down the page to the lyrics, I had a strong emotional reaction. When I settled down to sleep that night, I was overcome with nausea and chest tightness. It was grief, and it was refusing to be tucked away as I had instructed it to do. Grief can be disobedient. Grief is also wise.

I got out of bed and went into our spare room, journal in hand. I realized that this song was tucked away in a broken part of my heart. Reading the lyrics or hearing them conjured up great loss. It reminded me of all my former hopes, dreams and imaginings for my life. Flashes of memories came to the surface, memories of being full of baby and preparing for the gift of being a parent. There I was, right back on the sofa in our old house, wearing my favourite periwinkle maternity top and the blue jeans with the panel to hold my belly in place. This provided me with a momentary reprieve from the grief I had been feeling, and allowed me to tap into all of the remembered joy, excitement and innocence of being a first-time expectant parent. I could "feel" it once again: the awareness of changes in my body and mind coupled with the knowledge that, on some level, life would never be the same. I remembered how it felt to have the profound awareness of the magnificence of it all!

Over the years, I have learned that I will not drown in my grief. I have learned to allow tears to well up, knowing that they will eventually stop. No one has ever died from crying, and no one has ever cried continuously for years. In the past, in an attempt to avoid the sometimes overwhelming feelings of grief, I would stubbornly repress them. This would lead to other physical and mental discomforts, aches and pains. Eventually, I learned that grief is an important part of this journey. Although I will never be done grieving about it all, the more I allow it to surface and transform into something useful for me, the less intense it gets.

There are some losses that will never be okay with me. I have processed them as much as I can. To this day, there are tears that continue to find their way to the surface about the things I will never have, but I have accepted them to the best of my ability. Recently, I overheard a conversation between my dear friends and their eight-year-old daughter. I had spent the night at their home and was in the next room gathering my things. They were having a discussion about their plans for the day as a family. Would they go for a ski, or maybe stay indoors and watch a movie, or maybe just take a walk? I listened to them discussing their options and my eyes instantly filled with tears. Oh, what I would have given to have a conversation like that with Meredith.

If people have told you to "get over it," "move on" or "stop grieving," ignore them. They mean well. The fact is that you will always have grief but you will learn to live with it. It will lose its power over you in time, and your life will eventually not be defined by this grief. Its presence will soften, and you might start to feel, occasionally or even most of the time, that your grieving process is complete. Years may pass, and then, all of sudden, a song, a conversation or another reminder will bring those emotions back to the surface.

Just a few weeks ago, I was invited to a baby shower. As the honouree unwrapped her gifts, I felt a pull in my chest as the paper came off one box revealing a high chair that was similar to the one I received as an expectant mother so many years ago. I remember looking forward to using this generous gift with our new baby, but after the reality set in that our girl would be exclusively G-tube fed, the high chair made its way to our basement. It remained there for years, never unpacked or used. Seven years after my birth, I met a couple in the prenatal classes I was teaching. They were struggling financially and we decided to give them our high chair. It was a bittersweet day when we hauled it out of the basement and handed it over.

We need to befriend our grief. It doesn't have to be a dark cloud that hangs over us or that we try to stay one step ahead of. Grief can be our silent companion, something to be tended and nurtured. Think of grief as a person knocking on your door who really wants to see you. They knock incessantly, and you duck behind closed curtains praying they'll take the hint and leave. But they don't. Instead, they just keep on knocking until you finally swing open the door exclaiming, "WHAT DO YOU WANT NOW?"

When the knocking starts, instead of hiding, you can take a deep breath and welcome this person into your home. You set a few reasonable boundaries as to how much time you have to give, and then you put the kettle on. You settle in for some hot tea and conversation. As the visit progresses, you notice that it isn't as bad as you thought it would be. You are discovering that this person you had always hidden from is wise and has much to offer. Then the time is up, and although you found the visit surprisingly helpful, you are exhausted and have a list of things to do before the day ends. You say your goodbyes knowing that this person, whom you now consider a friend, will be back. They may return when it isn't convenient, and you may not want to stop what you're doing to sit quietly and share tea. But you have learned the value of this pause in your day with this friend who has only your best interests at heart.

In the beginning, there will be many losses and they will seem to surface constantly. You might wonder how you could ever grieve for all of it, and how it could ever be possible to feel happy again. Happiness will return if you welcome grief into your home and give it your attention. Slowly but surely, this will help you to stop feeling consumed by the grief. The visits will become less frequent and less exhausting. You will find that, in grief's wisdom, letting go of things you once had or dreamt of having makes room for amazing possibilities you were unable to see before. The process of grieving leads you, eventually, to a place of deep gratitude.

When grief visits, you might find it helpful to invite others along. Spending time with grief in isolation can be overwhelming. A trusted friend, a parent who understands what you are going through, or even a therapist or a support group can all stand witness and offer nurturing and caregiving to you as you sit with grief. It takes practice to be a host to grief. In time, you will become an expert on the things that work for you and on how to make the process of grieving more comfortable. These things may change over time.

I have learned that our intellect can be very convincing when it comes to coping with loss. We delay the natural evolution of our grief when we stifle it, shame it, intellectualize it and judge it. Trust that the deeper you allow yourself to know your grief, the deeper the joy you will feel when grief's visits get further and further apart. There is no barricade large enough to keep grief out. Welcome it with open arms, serve it warm tea and sit with it without judgement, knowing that grief will come and then it will go, as long as you give it the attention it needs.

CHAPTER 20

The Freedom of Forgiveness

Every single one of us will have something happen to us that will leave us hurt, broken, betrayed and angry. Someone will do or say something to us that we will deem unforgiveable, and we will stand by that conviction as though our lives depend on it. There is power in our rage and when someone has crossed us, directing that anger towards the source of our pain feels good. It can soothe the immense powerlessness we felt when the unforgiveable occurred.

If you are human and interact with other humans, then you have been wronged. You cannot go through this life without having an offense committed against you (whether real or perceived). We cannot control what others end up doing to us, whether it's an unfaithful lover, a friend who steals from you, or a stranger whose negligence changes the course of your life. What we *can* control is how we will respond and move on from the event that has caused us such pain and hurt.

Let's face it, it feels counterintuitive to forgive someone who wasn't overly concerned with your feelings to begin with. Why would we soften our hearts and set them free when what we really want to do is punish them and make them pay for what they have done? It is natural to want to seek revenge but in reality, as you seethe and fantasize about how you can get them back, they are probably carrying on with their lives oblivious to how their actions ultimately impacted you. The only person who is suffering is you. This may be why you believe revenge will make you feel better – but it won't. The whole "eye for an eye" theory never ends well. There might be temporary relief, but you will soon find yourself in the same boat you were in before you sought revenge. With that said, fantasizing about creative ways to get back at the betrayer can be therapeutic to a point. Just don't act on those fantasies.

Forgiveness is difficult because for the most part, we don't want to forgive. For many of us, forgiveness means that we are no longer angry, that we understand why the offense occurred and we are okay with what happened.

For these reasons, most of us can never truly forgive. Forgiveness, though, is actually none of the above. Forgiveness doesn't mean that you're okay with what happened but that you're making a decision to no longer be imprisoned by it. It means you are not going to be defined by the event nor by the dark emotions that accompany it. It means that you are no longer going to put your energy into fueling the fires that were ignited by another person's wrongdoing.

Forgiveness does not mean that you forget what happened. Instead, you store that event with all the other hard-earned lessons from your life, so that you can recognize when a similar situation may be unfolding.

To reach a place of forgiveness is a process. It takes not only time but action. Thinking about what happened and letting it roll over your mind again and again will help you to make some sense of it. It also helps if you share your story. A non-judgmental friend is invaluable, although a therapist can ask specific questions to help you dig deep and unearth insight you might not have considered before. For the big, earth-shattering betrayals, you will need to practice serious self-care. Surrounding yourself with people who love you and can help you navigate the aftermath is paramount. The expression of the deep, primal emotions that are a part of this loss is extremely important in eventually moving past it.

Writing a letter to the betrayer can be cathartic by giving your pain a voice. I used to suggest this in my "Making Peace with Your Birth" workshops. Set some time aside where you can be alone with your thoughts, sit down with pen in hand and hammer it out. Put it all on paper. If the tears come, let them smudge the ink but do not stop. Get it all out. This letter is not to be sent but is used as a way to really connect with the raw feelings around the betrayal. You can destroy this letter through burning, for example, or you might want to keep it to read at a later time. It might act as a measure of how far you have come.

I found the use of rituals to be particularly therapeutic in recovering from betrayal and eventually getting to a place of forgiveness. You must work through a substantial amount of the emotion connected to the wrongdoing before the rituals can work their magic. For me, fire is a natural "go-to" in my rituals, but you can also use other elements like water (dissolving paper in water, or tossing stones that you have attached meaning to into a river, lake or ocean), earth (burying something or planting a seed for renewal) or air (blowing out a candle). Actions like tearing or shredding paper items, breaking and smashing more-concrete items, or physically crossing a threshold – like walking through a doorway or stepping over a rope – are all rituals that can help you to achieve the intention of releasing and letting go of a person or circumstance. What is most important is that your ritual is meaningful to you. The purpose of rituals is to pluck you out of ordinary time and give you space to use physical actions to bring some sort of healing to your heart.

Getting to a place of forgiveness requires your attention. It requires your willingness to, at the very least, *entertain the possibility* that you will eventually come to a place of forgiveness. Forgiveness is an action of the heart as opposed to the mind. Setting the intention to forgive is intellectual, but really feeling the act of forgiveness is most certainly rooted in your heart and emotions. You may have a long list of people who need forgiving. Start with the one that causes the most heartache. You may need to go back to the day of your child's birth. If there was negligence by the doctor or midwife, you may consider taking legal action. If you do, this will not change your child's birth or outcome, and it will not cleanse you of your anger and sadness. You still may discover that to fully recover and heal, you will need to take some of the steps I have suggested to come to a place of forgiveness. Remember, this does not mean that you are okay with what happened or that you are letting the person off the hook. It simply means that you are no longer going to allow the toxic aftermath to permeate your being and your life.

One of the most important people to forgive is yourself. We all carry guilt about things that we have done or didn't do, and this can be a heavy burden to carry around with us. You can do all of the same things to reach a place of forgiveness for yourself. It is possible and necessary.

I have learned that it takes a lot of energy to hang on to ill feelings towards another person, even if they seem completely justified. When I am able to find the compassion within myself to release those who have wronged me, I can practice the ultimate in self-care and self-preservation. Ironically, when I set someone else free from my resentment and anger, I free myself.

CHAPTER 21

Being Resilient for the Long Haul

If you have gotten this far in this book, you may have come to the conclusion that you are not coping well with the stress of raising a child who requires extraordinary care. You may have resigned yourself to the fact that you are just not strong or naturally resilient. If I had a dollar for every time someone claimed that they couldn't do what we were doing, I would be a wealthy woman. I understand the sentiment because I too never imagined being as strong as I've become.

You may not have been born resilient, but you can learn. You will have to learn resilience if you want to be healthy in mind, body and spirit for the duration of your parenting journey. You may think to yourself that I don't understand your dire situation, or you may have concluded that my situation is not as bad as yours. Maybe you simply feel so overwhelmed at the moment that the concept of resilience is impossible to even contemplate. Hear me out. Know and trust that resilience is possible and can be achieved. It may not have been your habit to excel in the face of adversity, but you can hone these skills and be resilient for the long haul.

I also know that each of us has limits and that these differ from person to person. Some people are more naturally resilient than others. Each of us carries within ourselves a unique lifetime of experiences that have impacted our health and well-being. Added to our genetic blueprint, they make us who we are. No matter who you are there are some powerful-yet-simple ways to improve your health and to ensure your resilience in the long term, and they can be incorporated into your life starting today. Resilience is dependent on caring for yourself. In addition to the tips on self-care in Chapter 8, there are many ways you can boost your resilience.

The Pity Party. It is nearly impossible to parent full-time for the long haul without allowing ourselves the odd "pity party," as I call it. A pity party can also be called a mini-breakdown (or breakthrough). It is a need to draw inwards, curl up and feel lousy about everything. This practice of collapsing under the weight of it all can be just as gratifying, healthy and beneficial as diligent self-care; it can be as though you are laying your battle armour down, falling to the ground and resting in a fetal position. It can also come unexpectedly and viciously, catching you off guard. However it comes, a pity party is both unavoidable and necessary if we want to keep moving forward on this path.

One of my more memorable pity parties occurred in 2012, when Meredith was nine years old. I had grand plans for a glorious, much-anticipated night away by myself. I would spend the day wandering around a quaint area of the city, getting together with a friend and her new baby for lunch, then meet two other friends for Thai food in the evening. My plan was to stay overnight and sleep in. Oh, how I craved that possibility! The next day, I would wander, taking my time to get home. This time away had been planned for a couple of months, and getting two busy friends and myself freed up for one night was quite a feat.

But a winter blizzard stopped me in my tracks. The skies opened up, and freezing rain and blowing snow sealed my fate. I was remarkably furious. I really, really, really wanted, needed and looked forward to a night away from home.

Thankfully, I had a plan B! I checked with my friends and, sure enough, they were free the following Friday. So, I spent one more week looking forward to our big night out. Finally, Friday came, and before I knew it I was on my way to 36 hours away from home! Because my van started making unfamiliar sounds, I drove my husband's car instead of mine. You know where this is going …

I arrived at my destination and headed for my favourite lunch spot. It was such fun to sit and quietly eat lunch, uninterrupted. Then I was on my way to my favourite bookstore. The day was going perfectly, until the car started wobbling as I drove down the street. The wobbling seemed worse when I drove slowly. Since I was stopping by a friend's house, I had her partner take it for a drive to see if he could tell what was wrong. It turned out that the car was in need of two new tires and was not safe to drive.

My planned afternoon of strolling casually around the city was no longer to be. Instead, I would have to spend the afternoon bringing the car in and waiting for the job to be completed, then race across town to get to my friend's house by 6:00 p.m. I was really angry that my second attempt at having 36 hours to myself was being compromised.

Jessie, a dear friend of mine, suggested we go for tea while we waited for the repairs to be completed. I walked into the teashop, and the sweet salesperson approached us with some sort of herbal tea with a name like "Rainbows, Sunbeams and Unicorns," and I felt the rage in me start to bubble up. I walked out of the tea shop. I was ripping mad, and my friend, who has known me since I was 14 years old, suggested we just go for a walk.

She tried to console me and encourage me to see the bright side. Suddenly, I crumbled and began spewing out my frustrations. They sounded something like this: "I am sick and tired of always having to be strong and put on a happy face. I wake up every single bloody day with a smile on my face and a positive attitude. I spend every minute of every day caring for someone else – our daughter, our daughter's caregivers, my husband, the night nurses, clients, friends, family. And the one day, *the one day* I plan to just relax and hang out, the stupid (insert swear words of your choice here) car had to break down. It couldn't break down on the other 45 days my husband has driven it in the last two months. Oh no, that would have been too convenient!"

At this point, I was feeling quite sorry for myself. I was snottin' and bawlin' and having a full-on pity party. My dear friend walked beside me, allowing me the space to just pour out everything that was in my heart, every frustration, rage, heartbreak and annoyance. She did not "yabut" me, ask questions, interrupt me or attempt to console me. Instead, she picked up a gigantic piece of icy snow and fired it at a tree with a growl, encouraging me to follow her lead. After some hesitation, I followed suit. It felt great and then I started laughing. My pity party was short-lived, but powerful and necessary.

Time has passed, and my pity parties have become fewer and far between. But we all need to allow ourselves the odd pity party. Fighting the urge to flop on the floor for a good bawl simply creates chaos within ourselves. We have to surrender to feeling crappy instead of trying to "get over it." When I used to get angry and impatient with myself for not feeling more positive, things just got worse. When I admitted that the situation really sucked, it gave me permission to feel terrible. Sometimes, that small shift was enough to lift my spirits.

Putting Yourself First. We can easily be consumed by caregiving and convince ourselves that it is impossible to nurture ourselves and our own interests and hobbies at the same time as caring for our child. To be resilient for the long haul, we must sometimes put ourselves first. That might go against everything you have ever been taught about selfless caregiving and parenting, but I cannot stress enough how important it is to not lose sight of who you are aside from being the parent of a child with extra needs. Particularly during the early days, when the stress and shock are at their peak, our authentic self, the one that is separate from mothering and being a partner, gets buried somewhere. It is paramount for all mothers (and fathers) who are long-term caregivers to stay in touch with that part of themselves.

If you are interested in interior design, for example, you can find ways to stay connected to your interest and your passion, even if this might begin only with splurging on an interior decorating magazine or creating a scrapbook of things that appeal to you. Each of us can do something to fulfill ourselves. It just takes a bit of creativity and patience, as the solution may not come to us right away.

Create a vision board, a collage of pictures and words depicting your dreams and aspirations and the things you enjoy. Start with just five minutes and build on it. You will soon begin to crave these five-minute retreats. Gradually increase the amount of time you spend. You will see that not only does the world stay intact while you focus on yourself, the world actually looks brighter because your perception has shifted ever so slightly. You deserve that time, and your family deserves to have you feel that you are worthy of time for yourself. Whatever it is that feeds your soul, start now to keep that part of YOU alive.

Remembering to Breathe. We breathe approximately 23,000 times per day. I have held my breath a lot over the past decade.

I held my breath in that moment when Meredith was born.

I held my breath as I gently but firmly ordered her to breathe and to stay with us while I flicked the soles of her feet and the midwife administered oxygen.

I held my breath that morning, five days later, when the words carefully tumbled out of the neurologist's mouth: "… as I suspected, your daughter has suffered a serious brain injury."

I held my breath every single night we had to leave Meredith in the NICU and go home to our empty house.

I held my breath each time she was poked, prodded, and crammed into an uncomfortable position for an X-ray.

I held my breath when, only six weeks after she was born, the pediatrician told us they would be making an incision in Meredith's abdomen to insert a feeding tube. I held my breath as they wheeled her down the hall for that first surgery and for every surgery after that.

I held my breath when we left the hospital to bring her home for good. How would we ever know what to do with her all on our own?

I held my breath each and every time she violently retched from the severe reflux that plagued her ... up to 15 times in 24 hours. Each time, I held my breath, urging her to catch hers.

I held my breath during each follow-up appointment for fear that there would be even more bad news. Good news is hard to come by when dealing with a complex brain injury.

I held my breath the first time Meredith stopped breathing for no apparent reason and we called 911 and endured that long wait for the ambulance. I held my breath during the bumpy ride to the emergency room and as we waited for her to come back to us. She did come back, both then and the other six times she stopped breathing.

I held my breath when we were told that her life would be short, and I held it again when we were given a cheerful tour of the palliative care home for children.

I held my breath each time a new professional entered our lives. Sometimes, I held my breath due to the exhaustion of explaining everything for the 250th time, and, at other times, I held my breath to keep myself from wringing someone's neck.

I held my breath every single time she screamed out in pain and anguish from things most people take for granted, like pooping and eating.

I held my breath to avoid flailing on the floor and screaming with heartbreak as I witnessed her pain.

I held my breath, over the course of more than eight years, every single time I held her in my arms and her arching and constant thrashing forced this one rib of mine to pop out of place.

I held my breath when we made the difficult decision not to have more children. I was certain that if I fully faced the reality of that decision, I would shatter into a bazillion tiny fragments. So, I held my breath instead.

I held my breath through every festive holiday and event, such as Christmas and Halloween, knowing that Meredith could never fully understand what these holidays were all about.

I held my breath as I lay in bed, listening to hear if the nurse was getting to Meredith when she retched or cried in the night.

I held my breath as I lifted her while she had her fiftieth seizure of the night, even though what I really wanted to do was slam my fist through a wall. Holding my breath kept the rage at bay.

I held my breath to hold back the tears. Oftentimes it was not possible to shed them, and I couldn't bear to burden her with her mama's tears plopping on top of her head.

I have held my breath too many times to count over the last 14 years.

I wasn't really aware of how much I was holding my breath until I started having "episodes" when I couldn't catch my breath. These usually happened when I was running upstairs or exercising. It was sudden, frightening and puzzling.

I underwent just about every test available to determine what was happening to me. It wasn't until the fall of 2014 that a physiotherapist gave a name to what I was experiencing: chronic hyperventilation syndrome. It is caused by dysfunctional breathing patterns, usually as a result of deep, unrelenting stress. I suspect that many parents of children with medical fragility do a lot of breath-holding. Upon reflection, I recognized that I held my breath quite often over the course of the day. Since having this awareness, I re-learned how to breathe properly from my belly, using my full diaphragm, as opposed to breathing only from the upper portion of my lungs. It has been a hard habit to break and I continue to check in with myself regularly to make sure I am not holding my breath.

I wish someone had told me to be aware of this when we first landed in the NICU all those years ago. I wish I understood the importance of conscious breathing and how disorganized breathing can lead to other issues like low-grade anxiety or even panic attacks in extreme cases.

Simply mastering your breath and feeding oxygen to the body's many systems is an easy, efficient way to contribute to overall resilience. It's an opportunity to relieve stress every single time you take a breath. Think about that for a moment. I thought it seemed far too basic to be effective, until I was forced by my own health to pay attention and found out that it works.

Lastly, be gentle with yourself. Think of yourself as a work in progress and commit to making gradual changes. Your body and mind will respond quickly, and you will soon discover that the more you nurture your resilience and practice self-care, the easier it will be to respond to whatever life challenges come your way. Just do what you can at this time. Sometimes the smallest shifts produce the greatest benefits. If you are enduring a long hospital stay with your baby, for example, staying hydrated and fed may be the only self-care you can manage. This is enough. Keeping it at the forefront, and re-evaluating your self-care habits on a regular basis, can make an enormous difference in long-term resilience.

CHAPTER 22

Accumulating "Thrival" Skills

To thrive in the midst of debilitating stress, exhaustion and, at times, overwhelming fear, is both a challenge and a goal. To achieve this, you need to make a commitment that, no matter what, you will not merely survive. You will face the future with a sense of hope and optimism that helps you to thrive and to live your life fully.

The years since our daughter was born have been deepened by experiences that never would have materialized had I not mothered Meredith. I have learned so much about myself – my body, my mind, my spirit – and about the world and life. Originally, I thought that a million other circumstances could have afforded me the profound lessons I have learned, but I think differently now: no one but this particular child could have helped me grow as a person better or faster.

You may be at the beginning of this part of your life story. You are going to have days when you feel as though you are suffocating, and you will truly and passionately believe that there is no way you will survive whatever particular challenge you are facing. You will believe that. Will you survive the day by lying down and letting your world collapse around you? Perhaps. You're allowed to have the odd pity-party day.

Thrival skills include seeking out whoever can give you relief, guidance and support: a therapist, a body worker (chiropractor, massage therapist, etc.), a personal trainer, a spiritual guide. You will need to attune to your feelings and your body if you want to stay well for your child. You will also, with time, begin to learn the cues, even the non-verbal ones that will allow you to figure out what your child needs. You will develop a sixth sense that will help you determine, with 99 per cent accuracy, the problem or discomfort affecting your child.

You can also develop a sixth sense about your own needs. Perhaps your chest feels tight and heavy. Rule out any obvious medical issues, then sit down in a quiet place, put one hand over your heart and just sit there. If you sit long enough and breathe into the discomfort, your eyes will soon fill with tears. Allow yourself to cry. Do not be afraid to tap into that sadness. Let those tears come. Give yourself the space to release them. They will eventually stop and relieve the pressure in your chest. When you feel that tightness building again, repeat this process.

I was intrigued by a comment left on my blog about my use of the word "surviving" when describing the many experiences we go through as parents of children with extra needs and, more specifically, with medical fragility. The author of this post, who had a friend with disabilities, thoughtfully expressed the opinion that saying we had "survived" implied "burden and suffering and other negative things." She felt that the woman's family would never use the word "survive" to describe their experience raising their daughter.

This comment got me thinking about the use of the word "survive." I thought about what it meant and if, in fact, I (or the thousands of other parents of children like ours) had actually "survived" anything at all. Perhaps I was being somewhat melodramatic. Perhaps there was a word of lower intensity that could have been used in its place.

There are several definitions of the word "survive": to continue to exist; to stay alive despite an injury, illness, war, etc.; to manage to deal with something difficult or unpleasant; to continue to function or prosper; to cope with (a trauma or setback); to persevere after; to continue in existence after (an adversity, etc.). And then I thought about some of the experiences we have had, which include, but are not limited to:

- A traumatic birth where I called out our newborn baby's name and encouraged her to stay with us as I watched her struggling to take in air while she was still attached to the umbilical cord;

- An abrupt separation within minutes of birth;

- The 70 days in a row (or 1,680 hours, or 100,800 minutes) when we lived apart from Meredith when she was a newborn. We travelled the 56.3 kilometres (35 miles) between our home and the children's hospital every day to sit by her side, not knowing initially if she would live at all;

- Seven sudden episodes of respiratory distress in a five-year period, resulting in frantic calls to 911 and long moments of waiting for an ambulance to arrive, not knowing if this would be the episode that she might not survive;

- Filling out DNR (Do Not Resuscitate) forms, a not-so-gentle reminder of the reality of the odds that we will likely outlive our daughter;

- Experiencing more than 365 days of broken sleep in a row, including eight or more months of waking every 1.5 hours to start or stop a feeding and dealing with severe retching episodes in between feedings. Managing care during the day, as well as at night, on less annual sleep than most people get in a month;

- The physical and mental demands of holding, carrying and lifting a growing child for eight and a half years, or 3,104 days (it seems much longer than that!), without the assistance of a wheelchair or any other device that she would tolerate; and

- Countless hospital stays, medical emergencies, surgeries, and all of the miniscule daily occurrences that affect her health and quality of life.

Most or all of these experiences surely come under at least three definitions of the word "survive." The use of the word "survive" does imply "burden and suffering." The word "burden" is defined as "something that is emotionally difficult to bear or a source of great worry or stress." We generally think of the word "burden" in a negative light. If something "burdens" us, it weighs us down and, if given the choice, perhaps we would rid ourselves of this burden, whatever it might be.

Technically speaking, I suppose that by saying we have survived, I am indeed implying burden and suffering. Frankly, many moments, days and even weeks were, and still are, difficult to bear. Caring for our sweet daughter is a source of great worry and stress. The burden of my mothering journey has little to do with our daughter having disabilities. Seeing her struggle and knowing she will never walk, run, dance, talk, sing, hug, and swim on her own burden my heart sometimes. If Meredith could speak, I believe she would agree that some of the things she is forced to experience and survive in this life are a burden for her too.

Celebrate the great moments while knowing that they won't last, just as the terrible ones won't last either. Develop a sense of humour. You will be grateful to have it when dealing with the challenges that lie ahead. You are going to need it. It may sometimes serve as a form of denial, but if it can help you get through to the next morning, then laugh away!

You do not want to sail through this parenting experience with "I will survive this" as your motto. You can do better than that. A happy and fulfilling life where you thrive amidst the chaos is a goal worth striving for.

What I would tell you
. . . about family life

CHAPTER 23

Celebrations and Holidays

I was raised in a fairly traditional home. We celebrate the holidays like most people in our small Ontario town. I have joyful memories of Christmas, Easter, Halloween and birthdays. My parents always made my siblings and me feel loved. Even when money was tight, they made sure there were presents under the tree and special treats. As I grew older, the magic of these occasions faded, yet I always knew that if I had children, I would get to relive my childhood through their experiences. This was something I very much looked forward to.

Our first Christmas with Meredith was spent navigating the NICU until mid-February. In that first year following her birth, we fumbled our way through the motions of each holiday in a sleep-deprived, shocked state. The magnitude of what the holidays would come to mean hadn't hit us yet, as Meredith was still a baby. We didn't feel the loss until she was a bit older.

In the weeks leading up to her first birthday, and in fact each October for the first three years after Meredith's birth, I felt grief hover like a heavy fog and settle in until we celebrated her December 5th birthday. Every October, the unbearable loss of my dreams and imaginings would move into my bones, forcing me to face a life that would not unfold as I wanted it to. I did not fight this melancholy. I knew what it was and acknowledged this confusing grief. I sat with it, examined, welcomed and honoured it. Then, as swiftly as it had moved in, it would move out on the morning of her birthday. I would feel a sense of relief that we had made it through another year.

Meredith's original life expectancy of seven or eight years invaded the deepest corners of our minds, even though we chose not to focus on it. Each birthday leading up to her eighth year felt as if we were moving towards Meredith's inevitable end. When Meredith turned eight, it felt magical, as if she had defied the odds.

As the years passed, birthday celebrations were less burdened with grief during the weeks before the big day or on Meredith's birthday itself. The tears we shed, if any, were no longer tears of sadness for what could have been, but tears of joy for what was and what would come to be.

Every moment since her eighth birthday has been a blessing. When Meredith turned nine, we no longer felt lingering, bittersweet emotions leading up to her birthday, nor did we experience a sense of grief as we previously had each year. Meredith's eighth birthday was extra special because we never thought it would come about. Meredith's birthday is now the major celebration in our home. It has become more important than any other holiday or celebration.

As much as I wanted to rejoice and celebrate the traditions of standard holidays during those years, I had a strong urge to crawl into a cave and retreat until they were over. The urge increased as the years went by. Initially, I put on a brave face and made the best of Halloween, dressing Meredith in costumes and taking photos, even though she was uncomfortable and probably confused as I wrestled a giraffe costume onto her or stuck rabbit ears on her head. Halloween involved sitting outside on our porch, handing out treats. Children banging on the door could wake Meredith. Each year, admittedly, I felt sadness as I watched excited children in their well-considered costumes and recalled the sheer thrill of dumping a pillowcase of sweet treats onto the living room floor. Each year reminded me of the experiences Meredith would never enjoy. It didn't help that social media was flooded with photos of other people's kids enjoying the holidays.

At Christmas, we started decorating our tree to show her the lights. Although she seemed interested at first, her interest faded quickly. I found myself decorating a tree that no one cared about and tearing it down as soon as the holidays were over. Each year, we would go through the motions of the holidays, ignoring the gaping hole in our hearts that comes on Christmas morning when you have a child who will never understand the anticipation of Santa's arrival and the opening of presents. Each year, we participated in family functions, donning enthusiastic faces while we patiently waited for the day to end so that we could exhale and feel relieved that another Christmas was over.

Some years we didn't even bother with gifts as Meredith remained the same developmentally. Over the years, we have purchased five Fisher-Price aquariums and three GloWorms. These have been two of her favourite toys, and after wearing them out, we just buy more. Christmas shopping has always felt like an obligation, and shopping in the newborn section each year has never been a joyful experience for me. Oftentimes I would get so frustrated at the lack of choice that I would just walk out of the store and end up buying Meredith some new books and pajamas. The thing was, she didn't understand the concepts of Christmas and gift-giving, and yet each year, I felt I had to go through the motions as though it were my duty as her mother.

Fourteen years in, I just take it in stride now. Some years I find something amazing, and other years we just don't bother with gifts. It has been nearly a decade since we had a Christmas tree and this year, I am feeling like I want to introduce this to her again and see what she thinks of the lights. I have learned to do away with expectations. The unpredictability of mothering Meredith has led me to a place of knowing that expectations can often lead to disappointment and unnecessary suffering. I choose now to see where we are in any given year and make plans knowing things can change last-minute.

When Meredith was only weeks old, I read an online article that was written as a letter to the friends and family of someone with extra needs. Part of it discussed the immense undertaking involved in travelling with medical equipment and supplies, and the enormous amount of planning needed to attend functions away from home. I recall thinking as I read the article that this wasn't us, that we would be different. But I was a new mother then and could not imagine that the baby in my arms would grow to almost my height and weigh 55 pounds. I also could not foresee that Meredith would not enjoy or even tolerate sitting in a wheelchair.

One of my favourite holidays has always been Thanksgiving because it is about gratitude, something that I have become more aware of with each passing year. We had managed to share this holiday with our two families each year, until the fall of 2013, just before Meredith's tenth birthday. That year, Tim's family dinner took place over 200 kilometers (124 miles) from our home, a distance Meredith could never have tolerated in her car seat. Tim attended his family's Thanksgiving celebrations while Meredith and I stayed behind. We knew firsthand from the previous Christmas that it was becoming increasingly difficult to care for Meredith when she was out of her environment. Christmas 2012 had involved holding her for more than five hours, and coping with the high level of activity and noise typical of a large family gathering. She is no longer a compact and versatile baby or toddler, so we have had to adjust our expectations accordingly. Despite having wanted to be different, we are now the family that cannot attend functions away from home.

For the first decade of Meredith's life, holidays and celebrations were cloaked in grief. Weddings brought sadness because we knew our girl would never grow up to be someone's bride. The delight of children at Christmas and Easter weighed heavily on our hearts. Eventually, we almost did away with Christmas altogether. We opted out of gift-giving and sponsored a family in need in our community instead. I stopped dragging a tree into the house, and the decorations remained packed in bins in the basement. We adorned the windowsills with white lights and celebrated the winter solstice. Gradually, I got rid of the copious amounts of Christmas decorations that we had packed away.

It hasn't been easy to come to terms with the impact our new life has had on the holidays. We have relied on our creativity to make things work for us. Smaller dinner parties have taken the place of large gatherings. We have accepted that sometimes we will attend celebrations without Meredith, knowing now that she is secure and well cared for at home. We don't expect our families to change their lives to accommodate ours. Some events can happen in our home, and others will take place elsewhere. When it's the latter, we may not be able to attend.

It took eleven years for us to finally get a grasp on the holidays. We manage to see our families as much as possible and accept when events are planned that cannot include us. Meredith's birthday is still the highlight of our year, and although the party is smaller than it was in other years, we still celebrate in a big way the simple fact that Meredith is still with us.

Creating new traditions, adjusting old traditions, and trusting that the holidays will eventually be joyful again helped me navigate those first years. In the end, there are no rules. We do what works for our family and our child. I suggest you give yourself permission to take a break from any holiday that overwhelms you. They come around every year, so take comfort in knowing that there will be other chances to take part when you are better able to enjoy them.

CHAPTER 24

Sticking it Out (for better or worse)

Imet my husband Tim in the summer of 1996, when I had come home for a holiday, and we dated. I was certain that I did not deserve such a gentle, loving man. He was handsome, a gentleman, and so respectful and genuine. What was I going to do with someone like that? I told myself that it didn't matter because I would soon be heading back to Vancouver Island, thousands of miles away. Our brief dating adventure came to an end when I hopped on a plane bound for Victoria.

A few weeks later, Tim announced that he was dropping everything – quitting his job, selling his belongings and breaking his lease, to fly to B.C. to see what the west coast had to offer. I was ecstatic and knew that he would be the last man I dated. A few years later, we were married, living in Ontario and starting a new life together. A car accident settlement left us with a wee nest egg to buy our first home. In February of 2003, we moved into a house that we planned to stay in for years to come. Meredith was conceived the first weekend after we moved in, and forty weeks plus five days later she was born at home, and if you're this far into the book, you know how that turned out.

Suddenly, our connection, the life we had created, the plans we had made and the dreams we imagined all unraveled right before our very eyes. Our broken hearts and shattered hope interfered with our ability to do what we had always done in the past, which was cling together, love one another and find our way.

We had seven and a half years under our belts and a solid, cement-like foundation, but that wasn't enough to bear the weight of the news that the life we'd planned was not going to be. Once the sheer shock of it all wore off, anxiety and depression moved in, and our days were made up of moments where we simply tried to survive.

When a couple has a child with medical complexities, family, friends, and even the social worker at the hospital will tell you that you need to communicate. People will rattle off statistics about the high rate of divorce among parents of children with disabilities or illness. We tell couples that this experience will make you or break you, and then we virtually leave them hanging. For the couples just starting out, we don't offer a lot of guidance and practical tips on how to keep your connection intact and intimacy alive even in situations where the natural tendency is to walk away from each other. Love is a good foundation but we also need tenacity, bravery and vulnerability to stick it out.

I recall a lunch date with my husband a few weeks after we got home from the hospital. We had been living at the Children's Hospital of Eastern Ontario for ten weeks, and now we were home and spring was upon us. My parents came to visit for the day and urged us to slip away for lunch. I wanted it to be like we were before Meredith was born. I desperately wanted to see a glimmer of "us." Instead, we sat across from each other, fragile shells of our former selves, awkwardly attempting to make conversation. Everything was difficult in those early days: sleeping, waking, eating, talking and even breathing.

Everyone going through a traumatic loss mourns uniquely. The how, why and what of grieving is very individual. Naturally, Tim and I coped very differently. Initially, he shut down, and I took on a "We got this" mentality. I became like a machine, obsessively trying to do it all perfectly and efficiently; whereas he moved further and further away from us and into himself. Five months after Meredith's birth, I had serious doubts that we would make it at all.

A move to my hometown and the promise of a new beginning seemed to jolt us out of the dark place where we had found ourselves. We bought an old home that needed lots of love and care to make it livable. We moved in with my parents while the renovations took place, and I think the extra support and care relieved a lot of our worry and stress.

Finally we moved into our new home eleven months after Meredith's birth, and it marked a new beginning. There is always hope in new beginnings. It was around this time that we started having people in our home to offer respite and therapies. This presented a new challenge to us. We knew we needed the help and we were grateful to live in a province that gave us financial support to employ relief workers, and yet as we received more and more help, we watched our privacy dwindle.

We fought against night nursing for a long time. The thought of having a person awake downstairs caring for our child while we slept seemed so unnatural and foreign that we just couldn't wrap our heads around it. Eventually, it became a necessity.

In spite of all we've endured over the years, we have somehow managed to find our way back to each other. The road hasn't been smooth. We have both experienced periods of depression when residual trauma surfaced and more issues needed our attention. We had to make decisions right from the start that we were going to hang on and stick it out no matter what. We were committed to our marriage and to Meredith.

In order to find our way back to each other, we had to be courageous and vulnerable and throw caution to the wind. I wish I could share one magic tip that made it all okay again, but when I look back, I know it was an accumulation of many things – plus sheer determination and stubbornness – that got us through the dark times and brought us back to a place of deep intimacy and friendship.

I think back to those early years, long before Meredith was even a twinkle in our eyes, and I applaud our willingness and naïveté to vow to love one another "for better or worse." The truth is, most couples never imagine that the "for worse" part can be really, really devastating. And to be clear, Meredith was not devastating to us. It's the suffering and struggles she's had to live with that have been bone-crushingly painful to witness.

We don't realize that marriage (or partnership) is a continuous exercise in creativity, soul searching and a never-ending expansion of our love. Just when you think you have it all figured out, you're forced to adjust how you operate within your intimate relationship. And that's under normal circumstances, let alone extraordinary ones.

I tend to be very solution-oriented and I am all about preventative health care. This means that I (we) took steps early on, knowing that this experience was going to change us as individuals as well as change our relationship.

The good news is, I don't think it is ever too late to make changes for the betterment of your relationship. If you have neglected your partner and have convinced yourself that there's no point in trying to save your relationship, ask yourself this: "If you could return to a harmonious, passionate, deeply satisfying relationship, would you?" If the answer is "Yes," then begin now. Every step you take, no matter how tiny, will generate positivity within your intimate relationship.

Here are some tried and true ways to stay afloat when you feel as though your marriage/relationship is drowning:

1. **Seek Counsel.** There is nothing like setting aside an hour to unload on an objective, non-judgmental listener. You don't want to go to just any counselor or therapist, though. Find out who, in your own community, is well educated and experienced with the complexities of parenting a child with extra needs and/or medical fragility. Don't be afraid to interview a few counselors over the phone and ask about their experience in working with couples and working with trauma and grief. Don't waste your time on someone who specializes in addictions, for example, when you are dealing with complicated grief and marriage distress.

2. **Go on Dates.** This tip may induce a sense of panic. Let it be known that a "date" does not necessarily entail dinner out on the town and four hours away from your child. This doesn't even mean you have to leave your house. A date is simply setting aside some time where the focus is on your beloved. Shut off the TV and put away those phones (the killer of all intimacy). It might include a bottle of wine, music and conversation. If you have been operating like zombies for the last two years, this will feel incredibly awkward and foreign at first. Awkward or not, do it anyway. If it means you just sit there staring at each other, it's a step in the right direction. Practice is necessary to find your way back to each other. Next time you do it, you might actually be able to talk. Start slowly if it's been a while. Putting pressure on yourself is not going to inspire romance. Watching a movie in an upstairs bedroom while our daughter is cared for downstairs has given us just a little time alone and a breather from everyone else. Be creative and set the intention to give of yourselves to each other. Even a fifteen-minute walk outside holding hands is better than nothing at all.

3. **Gestures of Kindness.** Take the initiative to let your spouse/partner know that you think of them even in the midst of unrelenting stress. In our early dating years, Tim and I used to indulge in Häagen-Dazs ice cream (Caramel Cone Explosion, to be exact). After Meredith was born, I would occasionally buy a container while grocery shopping. We would share this treat in the one hour we had together in the evening after Meredith was in bed and before the night nurse arrived. Long before parenthood, we used to give each other massages. Tim always loved having his head massaged,

especially because he is prone to headaches. In the years after Meredith was born, no matter how bone-tired we were, we would sometimes spend ten minutes before sleeping to give one another this gift of touch and love. Connecting for only ten minutes at a time helped us find our way.

4. **Sex.** I once had a family relief worker ask if and how Tim and I managed to maintain any kind of sexual relationship. She asked innocently enough, and yet it felt like an invasion into the teeny tiny amount of privacy we had left in our lives. First and foremost, there will be periods of time where you live like roommates and sex starts to feel like a thing of the past. If there is one thing that will depress a healthy, vibrant person, it is the slow and painful death of their sex life. Sometimes, though, it is depression that kills your sex drive. Sex is a crucial and vital part of a healthy relationship. The thing is, sometimes it is impossible to give and to get. In those times, it is critical that you still maintain some sort of physical connection. For example: kiss one another good morning and good night without fail, hug often, hold hands, turn off all technology and just focus on each other (see tip #2) and even tell your partner that if you weren't so bone-tired and messed up you would take them to bed and make them howl! Sometimes, you have to look after your own needs, and if that involves a vibrating, silicone sea creature from China, so be it. No shame in relieving stress with some self-love.

    Logistically speaking, we have had to let go of spontaneity and now plan our romps in the hay. When our daughter is out for an hour-long walk with one of her caregivers, we take advantage of our empty house. You learn to become efficient when time is short, and you also learn to be very, very quiet. We also bought a memory foam mattress and decided to forgo the bed frame, choosing to have the box spring and mattress right on the floor. This was a game changer. I highly recommend a memory foam mattress. There is a fan in our room, too, which induces white noise and masks "other" noise. My mother keeps asking when we are getting a "proper" bed, but that won't be happening anytime soon. That memory foam mattress on the floor has allowed for the rebirth of an active sex life.

    After a lot of time has passed without any sexual connection, it can be really difficult to get back in the saddle, but you know what? You just have to do it. And if it doesn't work the first time (stress, hormones, etc. can wreak havoc on a sex life), try, try again and again. You may need to work through tips 1–3 before embarking on this one, but know that it is possible to quench your thirst after a drought.

5. **Eyes Wide Open.** When you fall in love or make the decision to marry, you look at the person you are joining with and think they are pretty darn perfect. When life interrupts the great thing you have going, as it inevitably will, you quickly learn that this person you are with isn't all that perfect. In fact they are far from it, and the reality that we are all imperfect beings hits you like a Mack truck. Looking at your partner with open eyes and a fresh outlook can really help you through the dark periods. Digging a little deeper and giving them your compassion and understanding is one of the ways you will halt any kind of disconnection.

6. **Set the Intention.** There is risk involved in finding your way back to one another. If a lot of time has passed since you were the happy couple you originally were, then it is going to take courage. It can even feel easier to remain stuck and bitter. Make a decision that you are not going to be a statistic. Look at your partner and say to them, "I am in this for the long haul with you. I chose YOU and I love YOU. I know that we are very far apart right now, but I am not willing to let this go. I know that on the other side of grief, suffering, sorrow, anger and guilt, there is love – and there is 'us' and the essence of this beautiful thing we created." Vow to each other that you will stay right here side by side for as long as it takes to find your way out of the darkness.

As we found our way back to each other, we discovered that beneath the stress and exhaustion, the "us" remained. The love and passion we had for each other was still there, as was our sense of humour and the beautiful and unique connection we had made so many years earlier. We forgave each other for whatever needed forgiveness. We freed ourselves of grudges and old damage, knowing that we had been operating from a place of broken hearts, sleepless minds and worn bodies.

The truth is, sometimes you can want so badly to find your way back to one another and still it isn't enough. Sometimes one person is willing, while the other has one foot out the door and has already decided that they do not want to put the effort into trying to make it back to a place of harmony and love. You only have control over yourself and how you will conduct yourself in your relationship with your partner.

Fight for it, trusting that, in the end, if it all falls away, you can know in your deepest parts that you gave it your all. If you are reading this and your relationship did not survive under the suffocating stress that this experience brings, then tuck these tips into your pocket for when a new relationship is on the horizon.

Tim and I know that we have to remain vigilant when it comes to protecting our relationship. There will always be new stressors and unexpected detours in the months and years to come. We know that we may ultimately outlive Meredith, and if that time comes, navigating that tremendous loss will be monumental.

Your marriage/relationship will go through some harsh, frigid times, but this is not indicative of the end. You see, that is where many couples make one of the biggest mistakes. As soon as things get tough, they call it quits. We have learned that each time you triumphantly surpass the challenging times, you deepen your intimacy and you get to experience a love that you may have never imagined. There are gifts that come from the darkness, and only when you find your way through the darkness will they be revealed.

CHAPTER 25

Having More Children

Meredith was our first child. The decision about whether or not to have more children was one that needed to simmer for a while. We had to see how our whole experience with Meredith was going to unfold. Our primary consideration was how ill Meredith was and how much care would be needed to give her quality of life. With one exception, all the families we met in the early days had other children.

People openly shared their opinions about whether or not we should grow our family. One of Meredith's doctors bluntly told us that, since she was unlikely to live past the age of ten, we should consider having more children: "You know, to fill that void." He admired us as parents, and I think he felt badly for us, knowing that someday we would likely be childless. It seemed to weigh on him more than on us. I remember thinking it would take a hell of a lot more than a healthy child or two to fill a void as great as that left by the loss of Meredith.

At that time, I could not imagine being pregnant again, giving birth and then caring for a newborn. For the first eight and a half years, we had to hold our daughter. So, logistically, it seemed impossible to have another child. Our family members assured us that it would be busy for the first two years, but that it would soon get easier. Two years? I could hardly imagine getting through two hours on some days. Two years felt like an eternity. The well-intentioned logic was not winning me over. Not to mention the fact that we were in our early thirties when we had our first child. As time passed, I could almost hear the eggs in my body clanging down the pipes each month. When we found ourselves pushing forty, we knew that we had to make a decision.

The morning of my husband's vasectomy was a surprisingly difficult one. It symbolized the end of my childbearing years and the certainty that I would never experience mothering a healthy child. Never. I also knew that, without other children to care for, there was nothing to keep me here on this earth should something happen to Meredith.

I was well aware that our decision to get off the fertility train was one that impacted our families as well. They too grieved the loss of the children they had hoped we would have. They also grieved the losses we experienced, such as the chance to parent healthy children. Yet, we were the ones living this experience, and only we could decide if other children could fit into the life we found ourselves in. At times, not having more children did not feel like a choice we made, but rather a decision that was made for us.

In the first years after Meredith's birth, while working with childbearing women, it was difficult for me to share in their joy. There was always a veil of sadness draped over my smile. My younger sister was pregnant with her first child when Meredith was just under 18 months old. She and her husband invited me to be their doula. It had been almost two years since I attended a birth, and I was prepared to be a little rattled.

Ironically, I slid easily back into my role as a doula. I was overjoyed to discover that I still had my passion for the birthing process and that I was capable of practicing again the work I loved so much.

But I did not anticipate the upheaval of grief I experienced after the birth, when I witnessed my sister's new family recovering in my parents' home. I couldn't even bear to see them. So I arranged for breastfeeding help from elsewhere, as I knew my fragile heart might break to see them bask in their postpartum afterglow. It was one more example of how loss is not always evident right away and, instead, taps you on the shoulder when you least expect it. I witnessed my sister experiencing the postpartum period that I had imagined and envisioned for myself.

In the years since our daughter was born, I have marvelled at the wisdom of our psyches and emotions, as well as our ability to cope with whatever surfaces. Everything has its proper time. You cannot force those dark feelings into the light. They emerge when they need attention. It is our job to acknowledge, experience and feel the emotions, and then move forward.

Looking back, I know that the decision we made was the best one to make at the time, but I will never be okay with it. I hated having to make this decision in the first place. Knowing that, one day, I will likely be childless and past the age of childbearing makes me sad, extremely sad.

The losses Tim and I experience within our decision add up and intertwine with our daily lives. My husband tends to feel sadness at weddings, knowing that Meredith will never walk down the aisle. I am sad when I see my step dancing shoes, knowing that Meredith will never dance. She will also never have the awareness to ask about our histories, our adventures, or our love story.

I am reminded of the losses as I watch my nieces and nephew grow and develop, reaching milestones that Meredith can never, ever reach. My sisters and their families share a campsite on a lake for a few days each summer. They relate to the challenges of "normal" parenting. My older sister guides my younger sister through trying times and offers empathy and tips. Although all of us are close, our distinct parenting experiences have set us apart.

My youngest sister has four young, healthy and vibrant children. She is exhausted at the best of times, and completely comatose at the worst of times. I have been a sounding board for her while she navigated sleep deprivation, whining, teething, the terrible twos and the even more terrible threes.

I listen and empathize and sometimes, though rarely, I find myself wishing I could have those problems instead of my own. I am usually able to avoid this thought, to be objective and understand that her challenges at any given time are just that: challenging. Would I find it easy compared to what we've been through? I doubt it. I only spend a couple of hours in her very busy, noisy house, and then I can escape back to my home.

One day, after listening to her vent for days about the frustrations of her life as a mother, I lost it a little, and we had a fight. It was one of those fights that unleashed many years' worth of feelings. It was messy but necessary.

She explained that her complaints and negativity about motherhood were for my benefit. I had always swallowed my anger when hearing these complaints. I couldn't understand her lack of gratitude for the blessing of four healthy children. Her explanation surprised me. She told me that she refrained from sharing happy moments, such as her toddler coming downstairs dressed in a tutu and twirling around the kitchen in the sunlight, for example, because she didn't want me to feel bad about the fact I would never witness that with Meredith. She was attempting, in her way, to save me from the sadness that would most certainly befall me if she shared her children's achievements and accomplishments.

What she didn't understand was that this sadness will always remain for me. There is no way to protect me from feeling sadness because I do feel it, and probably always will, but its intensity has subsided. It is no longer waiting to spill over the edge into a puddle of tears. I have learned to befriend it, instead of denying it, and to recognize when sadness needs my undivided attention. I give it the attention it deserves by taking a day off, having a good cry or talking frankly about it, as I did that day with my sister.

The sadness does not consume me or run my life anymore. But it took time to get to this place of acceptance. It can take years. Like any great loss in life, letting go of the dream of what could have been takes time. What can bring you to this place of acceptance is acknowledging the loss, honouring the feelings that come with that loss, and caring for yourself in the process. Then you will be able to live with these sorrows, but they will no longer be at the forefront of your mind.

I now live vicariously through my sisters and friends. Sometimes, they call me to vent and to ask for my opinion about their children, and I feel that, in some way, I get to go along with them for the ride.

What I would tell you
. . . about seeing the bigger picture

CHAPTER 26

Letting Go and New Beginnings

All parents know that parenting involves sacrifice. But even more than sacrifice, parents of children with extra needs experience losses, both big ones and little ones. Besides the highs, the joys, the achievements, the celebrations, the "they-said-she'd-never-do-that-but-she-did" moments, there are also things that we have to let go of whether we like it or not. Depending on the level of care your child requires, you may have to let go of certain friends, an active social life, vacations, business travel or countless other options in life that parents of healthy children may take for granted.

In my mid-twenties, armed with a diploma in social work and searching for my purpose in life, I unexpectedly found my calling. At a woman's health fair, I discovered the doula profession. A doula provides continuous emotional, physical and informational support to a woman and her partner throughout labour, birth and the postpartum period. We differ from midwives in that we are trained to offer non-clinical care and are responsible for meeting the needs of the parents as they navigate through birth. Doula work is selfless, requiring one to be on-call and ready at a moment's notice; babies do not follow schedules, and due date predictions are often inaccurate. Babies often begin their journey in the wee hours of the night.

Almost twenty years ago, I embarked on the profound experience of being a doula. By the time I gave birth to Meredith, I had had the privilege of attending many births, but it soon became evident that I likely would not return to the doula work I loved so much. Although it was impossible for me to continue to work at full capacity, I always felt I would go back to it one day or, at the very least, I could keep up with other related work. I did attend births when one of my sisters or a close friend was having a baby, but I made peace with hanging up my doula hat for the time being. However, I continued to stay plugged into my work by teaching prenatal classes, making plaster casts of the bellies of pregnant women and offering workshops to women who had difficult or traumatic birth experiences.

In 2011, my heart and my intuition told me that life had other plans for me. I had a real urge to write and to reach out to other parents like myself through workshops and, eventually, through this book. It was nevertheless heartbreaking to let go of the part of me that existed before I started this incredibly challenging and uplifting journey of parenting.

A once-popular song on the radio claimed that "Every new beginning comes from some other beginning's end." I made a big decision then to let go of my certification as a doula and the majority of the classes I had been teaching. In doing so, I knew that I was creating space for what was to come – and whatever that turned out to be, it would be equally profound and life-changing. I know that I hung onto my work as a prenatal educator, even if just a few classes, as a gentle reminder that I had another life and another identity before the G-tube feedings, surgeries, life expectancies, medications, muscle spasms, wheelchairs, standing frames, therapies, children's hospitals, night nurses and family relief workers entered my life. There was more to me than "just being a mother of a child with extraordinary needs." I decided to fully embrace this role as mother and to carry all of the lessons I learned from my old life into this new one. And so, I let go … willingly, with heaviness in my heart, punctuated by waves of excitement, lightness and hope for who I was becoming.

It was a leap of faith, and for the most part I honestly didn't have a lot of faith at the best of times. When things were going well, I allowed myself to entertain faith and trust but when the tides would turn and our world would get tossed about like a glass boat near a rocky shore, I would lose faith all over again. In letting go, I felt I had nothing to lose. I could always re-train as a doula, re-certify and start over if I had made the wrong choice. My intuition was clear and booming too loudly for me to even consider that I was making a mistake. Still, I had doubts. I had to surrender it all and simply trust.

Fast-forward to a year later, when an opportunity presented itself in the form of a new career. I was designated as a marriage officiant, which set me on a new path that I could never have imagined taking. I immediately knew THIS was the path I was to follow. I felt the same sense of recognition and giddiness that I had experienced twenty years earlier when I first came upon doula work. In the fall of 2012, I enrolled in an eight-month, college-level, online training course and, in the spring of 2013, I graduated as a certified Life-Cycle Celebrant, specializing in funerals and end-of-life ceremonies.

This new career works well in our lives. Most ceremonies take place on the weekends when Tim is home and can care for Meredith. I have the privilege of meeting people and writing meaningful ceremonies for both big and small transitions in people's lives, from birth to death. I know this is exactly where I am supposed to be, and the work fulfills me.

You may need to let go of things in your life, things that you desperately want to hang on to, things that feel like a part of your identity. Often, familiarity and security keep us where we are and prevent us from growing and evolving. As a parent of a child with extraordinary needs, and depending on what stage of the journey you are at, you may think that your life consists of being consumed by the stress of caregiving. It may feel hopeless to imagine that things could change. This does not have to be the case. Be willing to let go of certain things to make room for the opportunities that are waiting on the sidelines. Grief is a part of letting go, even if it is for the best, and even if you are unsure whether letting go will lead to new beginnings. Every ending *does* lead to a new beginning, even if it doesn't feel that way at the time. There will be a new beginning. There always is.

CHAPTER 27

The Person You Will Become

In all honesty, I don't have a clue as to who you are becoming as a result of your experience. What I can tell you is that you will never be the person you were before this child landed in your arms or before you were given a diagnosis, either before or after the birth. I wish I could give you a guideline about how this experience will force you to grow, to expand your abilities emotionally, spiritually, mentally, and intellectually, and to stretch you beyond the limits you had previously set for yourself.

One of the most terrifying realizations in the early stages of this experience is that you are no longer the person you were. Your eyes and heart have been forced open to sights and emotions you may never have experienced before. You may also have experienced some level of trauma. This trauma may be rooted in your birth experience, the moments following birth or the countless times you've had to witness necessary procedures being performed on your child. Feeling helpless while your child endures unimaginable pain, for example, can be all it takes to leave a parent feeling traumatized.

You may be desperately trying to reconnect with who you once were. But your mission now is to get to know the person you are becoming. Your dreams and plans, everything you imagined your life with your new baby would be – all this has evaporated and can no longer be a reality. It is one frightening place to be!

The essential quality for navigating your way through these early months and years is knowing, deep in yourself, that you will survive, that you will have a life again and that, believe it or not, your new life will eventually feel normal. The life you once lived will begin to fade away, and you will slowly but surely adjust and thrive in this new life as a transformed person. It will not be easy. Nothing worthwhile ever is.

The process of transforming and transitioning into the person I am now has been so gradual. In order to see how far I have come, I have had to revisit places, see people I had not seen in a while and be transported to another time and place by such things as a photograph.

Eight years after our daughter was born, I was invited to speak at the annual general meeting of a local community services agency that had assisted us after Meredith's birth. On the evening I was scheduled to speak, a woman who looked vaguely familiar walked towards me. She was the infant development worker who came into our home and spent time listening to me while I shared my worries and fears as a new mother. She had probably never known how critically important her presence was to me. As soon as we embraced I broke into tears, realizing how much I had grown from the raw and vulnerable woman I was when I first became a mother.

A couple of years later, just a few weeks before Meredith's tenth birthday, I was overcome with an urge to return to her birthplace. I wrote a letter to the current owners, asking if they would be so kind as to allow me to return to the home I had left nine and a half years earlier as a broken and shattered new mother. On the last day before leaving that house, my mom, who was present at Meredith's birth, and I sat in that sacred space where Meredith was born, held hands and released tears over what could have been. Grief and shock hung like heavy drapery over every corner of every room.

I received a reply welcoming me to visit their home. Both relieved and hesitant, I wasn't sure what memories might surface when I walked back into the home where our lives changed so drastically.

Tim did not have the same need as I did to take this road trip and revisit the house of our past. However, my brother was visiting from Toronto and came along for support. I brought Meredith's first life album – which documents our pregnancy from the beginning right through to her G-tube surgery – and a journal, just in case I was inspired to write.

The gracious owners of the house had left us a note explaining that they had to go out unexpectedly, and encouraging us to have a walk-through as planned. The immediate familiar feel of the doorknob in my hand surprised me. I was stunned to walk into the kitchen to find that it had been completely renovated. The tile floors were gone, exposing the original pine boards which could be found throughout the entire house. The kitchen was completely unrecognizable from a decade earlier.

I walked into the open space that was once a dining room adjoining another larger room, which we had used as an office. Meredith had slept in the office during those first few fragile weeks at home when someone needed to keep constant vigil over her. The new owners had pulled back the red shag carpet in the office space to expose more pine flooring. The stark white walls of the living room and dining area had been painted a rich grey and a warm paprika colour. I remembered sitting on this floor with our infant development worker crying as I shared with her how difficult life had become.

I made my way to the staircase – an old, weathered, natural wood staircase. The hand railing that Tim installed for my safety during my pregnancy was still there.

I got to the top of the stairs and peeked into the bathroom. This was where I spent most of my labour. The bathroom had been updated and modernized. I looked towards the small, lone window, the window I had stared out of for hours as I rode out each contraction. I thought of the hard work that took place in that room on Meredith's birth day, and it made me smile. I felt calm and peaceful as I made my way through each room.

Finally, I entered the master bedroom. The queen-sized bed was positioned over the place where Meredith was born. I stood between the bed and the mirrored closet doors and closed my eyes for a moment. It was only then that I felt the tears surface and allowed them to fall.

I left a bottle of wine and a card for the owners and began to reflect on what my expectations for this visit had been. Perhaps I had expected the house to look the same. Yet, like the house, I too had undergone "renovations" and had changed. The shocked and shattered mother I had been had evolved into the confident, joy-filled, warrior mother I am today.

I needed to return to truly understand how far I had come. The visit helped me to realize that I had not only come to terms with my past, but also faced and embraced who I was in the present.

I understood that we must trust each experience we endure to bring us closer to the magnificent person we are to become. Growth begins by surrendering rather than fighting. When we have the courage to uncover the red shag carpet, we reveal our own polished pine boards.

In the early weeks and months after Meredith's birth, a low-grade anxiety permeated every cell in my body. I worried about how long we could possibly go on holding our child 15 hours per day. How would we cope with having a wheelchair and getting her in and out of it? What would puberty be like for her? As I sat, trapped on our sofa, holding Meredith and being overwhelmed by the future of my imaginings, something else was simultaneously happening under the surface. As each day unfolded, I was growing in strength and resilience and I was learning, slowly but surely, how to deal with each challenge as it arose. The more I faced each challenge head-on, the better equipped I became at taking so much of it in stride.

When the future I spent so much time worrying about actually came to pass, I discovered that I was able to cope with all of it. I hadn't counted on the evolution that would occur within myself. I would not remain the frantic, traumatized and fearful new mother that I was in the beginning. As Meredith grew and adjusted, so did I.

It is normal to be overwhelmed with fear and anxiety about what is to come. In these moments, remind yourself that under the surface, a transformation is taking place, and you will be equipped to handle each and every step of the way.

CHAPTER 28

The Sweet Spots

So much of this experience focuses on the hardship. Although it is critical to know how to navigate the difficult times, it is equally important to
understand how to recognize and value the sweet spots. The sweet spots are
those moments when you find yourself really living life in the moment. There
is an absence of extreme worry, maybe for the first time since you received the
diagnosis. In the beginning, there is a lot of worry and it is a daily struggle to
temper your anxieties so that you are able to function. It is almost unimaginable that a day will come when the intensity will settle down and you will
emerge from what seems like a deep, dark hole.

When you first experience a sweet spot, you may approach it with
suspicion. We grow so accustomed to endless stresses and unexpected
happenings that it's no wonder we are hesitant to exhale and believe that
maybe things are actually starting to look up for us and our child. You may be
waiting for the other shoe to drop. This is a normal response after being in a
hyper-vigilant state of mind for so long. The other shoe *will* eventually drop;
it's the nature of this parenting experience and of life itself. Your job is to learn
how to recognize and savour the sweet spots when they happen.

The sweet spots are easiest to recognize after a crisis. I remember the hell
of teething: sleepless nights, agonizing pain that could not be managed with
Advil or Tylenol, and a child who expressed her pain by physically thrashing
about until she was drenched in sweat. It was heartbreaking to witness,
especially because there didn't seem to be a whole lot we could do for her
but comfort her and wait for the tooth to cut. Since she does not eat orally,
cutting one tooth sometimes took many weeks. Then, just when we thought
we were at our breaking point, she would get some reprieve and consequently
we would, too.

The first decade was extremely hard and then without warning, everything
seemed to stabilize. There were periods where Meredith would have a head
cold or we would be without night nursing, but for the most part we entered

into a time that I knew was going to be our new normal.

The sweetest spot comes after some time has passed since the initial diagnosis. Everything seems to come together and life is no longer terrifying and overwhelming. It is when you recognize that, over and over again, you have proven that you can persevere no matter what has been set before you. You know that you are stronger and more resilient than you ever imagined and you can deal with anything. You have adjusted to whatever your child's diagnosis means for them, and everything that was once so foreign is now just a part of your child and your life.

This is the sweetest spot – when the diagnosis pales in comparison to the light of who your child has become. In the beginning, there is such fear to think that there could be something going on with your child. When the diagnosis comes in, it seems to change everything you previously thought about your baby. Suddenly they have a condition or an illness and that is all that can be seen. The sweetest spot comes when somewhere along the way, the diagnosis loses its importance and you discover this child who has been there all along. Their personality and their traits shine brighter than any diagnosis.

CHAPTER 29

Finding Meaning

I am not religious nor do I participate in any type of organized religion. I use the term "God" to describe the Life Force that I believe is part of all living things. We come into this experience of parenting with as many belief systems as there are parents of children with extraordinary needs. The experience can challenge all that we have previously had faith in, and it can transform our belief system profoundly. Some of us start out with very little faith, but find comfort in a Higher Power and even in attending a place of worship as a result of all that we endure and witness. Others might turn away from their faith temporarily or indefinitely because what has happened cannot be justified on the spiritual path they once travelled.

It took me many years to come to a place of peace. Since then, my spirituality has grown and evolved. Do I believe I was hand-selected by an All-Knowing-Powerful-Universal-Life-Force to mother this beautiful child? Not at all. I believe that what happened was simply life unfolding as it does. It does not matter whether or not I thought it should have happened the way it did. It happened. Yet, I knew that I was going to need strength from something greater than myself if I was going to mother Meredith with grace and humility.

In 2012, I travelled to Sedona, Arizona, in search of rest, rejuvenation and clarity. I needed to clear my head, sit down and meditate on one of Sedona's red rocks, which are reputed to hold power. I was hopeful that the energy of Sedona would give me the answers I sought. Meredith was showing mysterious symptoms that were not being managed well, and we felt desperate for answers that were nowhere in sight. I decided to visit the Chapel of the Holy Cross on the advice of Sedona locals. I was told the energy there was powerful because the chapel was built at the site of one of many energy vortexes surrounding the area. The following was written upon my return home from Arizona. It sums up how my feelings have evolved and changed, and how I have found meaning:

I felt You there upon entering the structure built into the red rock.

It was a spiritual place welcoming ALL, regardless of race or religion. Regardless of whether the toil of living had diminished faith.

I walked to the front pew, knelt and blessed myself – my Irish Catholic upbringing never far from the surface – and closed my eyes. I sat in silence and felt You there.

I sat with a blank mind, and then there it was … an image of a child's brain, black and grey and shattered, dull, heavy and lacking. I sat with this image, not questioning or judging it. I just sat with this broken brain until pink light flooded my mind. I observed this light as it swirled and danced around this small, bruised and beaten brain, bringing light and life to it. Then sparks flew and ignited long-forgotten pathways, connecting and breathing life and purpose into the damage. And I felt You there.

Your presence continued as I sat in this holy place and I felt the tug in my chest, the tightness opening and softening to let the tears bubble to the surface. And then I wept, and the tears found their way from my eyes to my cheeks, and I rhythmically brushed them away with my hands. And there I sat in calmness and peace, letting it all come up, letting it all go, leaving it all there, releasing it all to You.

I felt You there – all-powerful, all-knowing God/Goddess of the Universe itself; a perfect balance of female and male energy, nurturing and powerful and strong. I had felt Your presence throughout my life as a child and later as an adult, as I witnessed the extraordinary strength of a woman in labour and the births of countless children, all glorious and miraculous. I felt You in the enormity of the ocean, in the winds of a snowstorm and in the immense miracle of spring after the harsh winter. I felt You in the love I had for my husband and I felt You when we created our daughter. I have rarely felt You in man-made structures where you are reported to reside. But here we were, in the Chapel of the Holy Cross, You bringing me this energy, and me sitting, humble and grateful for what was moving through me.

The pink light swirled around the image of the healing and vibrant brain in my mind's eye, travelling across time and space, and I saw my daughter stretched out on her bed, resting as she would be at that very hour. I saw Your healing light swirling around her, enveloping her as she lay there, wondering where her mother had gone. And I knew that things were happening, that change was possible. I received confirmation that the answers I had been seeking were where they had always been ... within me. And I felt You there.

CHAPTER 30

This Privilege

In 2012, I provided a private prenatal session to a couple in preparation for the birth of their baby. Each of them suffered from a debilitating disease and had sustained ongoing health challenges for several years. Not only had they endured relentless physical side effects from both the disease itself and from the copious amounts of drugs used to manage the illness, they also had experienced tremendous psychological stress. Each had struggled with misdiagnoses and a lack of validation and confirmation, with all that this entails.

Yet, there they sat in my office, obviously in love and focused on the miracle of the pregnancy and their soon-to-be parenthood. This birth would be a normal event in two lives that had been nothing short of abnormal for many years.

I work from home. My clients must pass Meredith and her caregivers to get to my office. It is not uncommon for my clients to be curious about our daughter.

As I listened intently, they shared the hardship of having lifelong devastating diseases, and I found myself wondering, "How do these people face each new day? How do they continue to have such a positive outlook? I would lose my mind if I had to deal with what they are dealing with!" And then I laughed to myself, as I have had people say these exact words to me when they have learned about the details of having a child with medical fragility. As we continued to talk, the conversation turned to Meredith, and they wondered how we managed as parents of a child with such profound needs. I briefly talked about it and as always, I put a positive spin on it because, well, it really isn't the worst thing that can happen in a life. And they responded with, "I don't know how you do it!"

As we continued chatting, it occurred to me that those of us who perhaps are handed a bit more than the average person are privileged. You may assume that by "privileged," I mean "blessed" in some way, as if we were more than human. As if someone up there or out there thought us worthy of being granted a child with extraordinary needs – or in the case of this couple, almost unbearable illnesses – or a myriad of other unexpected outcomes, even catastrophes. But in fact I do not mean it in that way.

By privilege, I mean that when you endure something unimaginable, life can be experienced more deeply, with more succulence and less fear. You live with a greater sense of the fragility of the universe. You develop a perspective that only comes from riding out what you may previously have thought would be the end of you.

Your joys may be purer and may be experienced with more frequency, simply because you have also experienced tremendous sorrow and the kind of fear that only comes from close calls with death. You become acutely aware of things that may not be noticed by those who live a fairly ordinary life. You experience life profoundly and deeply because you have walked so close to the edge of life itself, knowing full well that it can change in a heartbeat. You are aware that life is short and can be gone in a flash. You know this in your bones, and you respond to life from this knowledge, which is always just under the surface.

You can choose cynicism and hate everything about your life because it just didn't unfold the way you wanted it to. This reaction may even be a healthy one initially, but if you get stuck there, you will be giving up so much more.

Maybe the secret of life is not so complicated after all. Perhaps it has to do with seeing the gifts that come from suffering, struggle and hardship. These gifts may be far less obvious, but also far more wondrous than one would expect. If given the chance, I would never relinquish this privilege.

What I would tell you
. . . the professional

CHAPTER 31

What You Need to Know

It is almost impossible to navigate this world of extreme parenting without the assistance of professionals. They may come in the form of doctors, therapists, nurses, social workers and teachers. Relying on so many experts is one of the more challenging aspects of our parenting experience. Over the years, we have grown accustomed to a steady stream of professionals coming into our home, and others meeting with us in clinics and in the hospital. Many have been with us from the start, watching us grow and adjust, and helping us meet the challenges that arise. Sometimes I wish I could give out a pamphlet to these professionals, describing the things that we appreciate, as well as those things that we are less fond of! It would include, among other things, the following:

1. **I do not think you are God.** There is far too much pressure placed on doctors. They cannot, and should not, have all the answers. Nor can they prevent catastrophic outcomes. As much as you deserve tremendous respect (as all of us do), you might be relieved to know that I do not hold you up on a pedestal or expect you to perform miracles. You are human, and I do not expect you to predict the future or a life expectancy. Nor do I expect you to know exactly what is going on with my complex child. I appreciate it when, with all your years of experience and knowledge, you can look at me and tell me that you do not know the answer. I do not need either shaky hope or dark predictions. What I do need is the truth as you know it, regardless of whether or not you believe I am able to handle it.

2. **Be aware of how long I have been on this path.** If we are meeting for the first time because my baby was born just days or weeks earlier, please keep in mind that I am exceptionally fragile right now. I am not only learning that my child will have lifelong issues, but I am also in the middle of the postpartum period. Please be mindful of my tender emotional and physical state. If we are meeting years into this journey, do not assume that I have become accustomed to the fact that there are DNR

(Do Not Resuscitate) forms in the desk drawer in our living room, in the glove compartment of our van and in our daughter's lengthy hospital chart. Please know that updating this form never gets easier. Speaking nonchalantly about our child's life expectancy is insensitive, whether you intend it to be or not. It will always be a delicate topic for us. Knowing that we will likely outlive our daughter will never, ever be acceptable to us.

3. **Meet me where I am.** Please do not expect me to be where you are mentally or emotionally, for I am not there yet. You have witnessed sorrows and losses that I have not lived through. I have not experienced even a fragment of what you anticipate for our future. I have only lived this life for a few days, a few months or a decade, and anything beyond this moment has yet to be lived. Use caution when sharing with us the medical outcomes of other families "like ours."

4. **Unless absolutely necessary, please refrain from asking me about my pregnancy and birth.** Especially in the early days, months and years, having to explain how and where our daughter was born each time we enter an emergency room, hospital or medical clinic becomes redundant and is unnecessary, especially when our visit is to rule out an ear infection. It is emotionally invasive to make us relive this intimate and personal experience with virtual strangers, simply in order to fulfill clinical checklists. Interestingly, by the time we have integrated this experience into that part of our brains that deals with difficult experiences, you will no longer have a need to ask.

5. **Understand that parents like me may have a dark sense of humour.** Although you might find this offensive at times, you will need to lighten up about something that is an effective coping strategy for us. When we live with this reality day in and day out, we cannot help developing a twisted perspective on things and finding humour in the most unexpected places. We do not need judging or scolding. The best thing you can do is laugh right along with us.

6. **Please assume that my spouse is as involved in our child's care as I am.** This may not be the case for some families. However, to be on the safe side, begin by assuming that my partner is as knowledgeable about our child's care as I am. Don't ignore him or her and do not question only one parent.

7. **Avoid feeble attempts at sharing unoriginal sayings disguised as hard-earned wisdom.** I once had a nurse tell me: "God will reward you." It is not appropriate to share these types of statements. Even if God does reward me, the thought of being awarded a trophy after I die for handling what life dealt me is not even remotely comforting.

8. **Our relationship is a balancing act.** I rely on your experience, knowledge, training and education to figure out each new challenge. We can accomplish so much more if you trust my experience, knowledge and intuition. Between the two of us, we should be able to find the answers, or at least know that we have tried everything we could to find them. Mutual respect for each other's expertise is critical.

9. **Do not take it personally.** Stress and sleep deprivation can bring out the worst in us. There are many days when I question my mental health and when I know I am hanging on by a thread. I may seem snappy, cranky and impatient. I work very hard at being "on" for everyone involved in our lives every single day and night. Please accept my apologies for the times I slip up. It is not you, it is me.

10. **Thank you.** I may not say it often enough, but I am grateful for you and the gifts you bring to our family. In the beginning, we learned from you, and because of your teachings, we were able to bring our medically fragile child home to care for her. Once at home, we were connected to therapists, nurses and social workers, and each of you contributed to the well-being and success of our new family. And you continue to do so to this day. We absolutely could not have made it this far without your guidance, concern, care and generosity. It is important that you know the work you do is valuable and is never taken for granted.

CHAPTER 32

Medical Equipment and Symbolism

Sometimes, I think back to the early years and I remember that, in some ways, they were easier. Meredith was smaller and more easily lifted and carried. She was a very sick baby who was always content to be held. She slept at night between severe retching episodes. In some ways, those early months after we got her home from the hospital were kind of normal.

There were, however, telltale signs that things were not normal in our home. For one, we had a shiny new IV pole that followed Meredith around and, whenever it wasn't hooked up to her, it stood at attention in the kitchen until her next feeding. The IV pole, a symbol of sickness, was the hardest piece of equipment for me to accept. I vividly recall the day the medical supply company delivered it, as though I had ordered it from the Sears catalogue and was excitedly awaiting its arrival. I remember how unwillingly I signed for it and how it looked to me all that afternoon, standing in the kitchen, wrapped in plastic. I couldn't go near it for a while. From the moment I made its acquaintance, I knew there was no turning back.

Similar feelings returned when Meredith's specialized stroller was replaced by custom seating in the form of a wheelchair. Meredith looked so proud and so very tiny in her big new chair! We clapped and cheered for her while our hearts broke a little more; the wheelchair symbolized immobility. It symbolized the stark reality that our girl would never run and play tag with her cousins, that she would never step dance like I had as a child or play hockey like her dad. She would never walk beside us, holding our hands.

We tried to create a space for her that did not resemble a hospital room. After all, technically, she wasn't sick. Honestly, we couldn't bear to put our child to sleep at night in a hospital bed. When the Make-A-Wish Foundation granted Meredith's wish for a brand-new bedroom in August 2012, one of my favourite aspects of the room was the fact that the designers installed a tall white cupboard with baskets that contained all of her syringes and medical supplies. We knew that Meredith would be spending the majority of her time in that bedroom, so we wanted it to be welcoming, bright and beautiful.

I loved the fact that when I walked into her room, it wasn't apparent that it was the room of a child with medical fragility. We didn't feel any aversion. We were not ashamed or embarrassed that our home looked somewhat like a hospital ward. We have felt many things over the years, but shame and embarrassment never took up residence in our vat of complex emotions. Our reluctance to welcome equipment and medical devices with open arms had more to do with stubbornness and, maybe, a sprinkling of denial. Perhaps hiding the obvious could help us imagine, to some degree, that things weren't as serious as they actually were.

Eventually, we had to accept that I could no longer carry Meredith upstairs or kneel on the floor to bathe her in a regular tub. We renovated our downstairs bathroom, installed a roll-in shower and bought a shower chair. By the time Meredith was approaching her tenth birthday, we realized that lifting and carrying her was becoming difficult. Her occupational therapist broached the subject with us but it was months before we could give the go-ahead.

As hard as we tried to keep things as visually normal as possible, the ceiling track was like a billboard, advertising the fact that our little girl was growing up and that we reluctantly needed to grow with her. As each year passed, it screamed at us that, if nothing was done, things would remain relatively the same in terms of Meredith's abilities and development; yet, she would continue growing and getting bigger. I felt that, soon, our little girl would be out of reach, as we transitioned into parenting an adolescent.

We all have things that symbolize this path. For me, that IV pole was it. For my husband, the ceiling track was just another kick in the gut that symbolized that life did not unfold the way we had imagined.

A note to professionals entering the homes of families like ours: there may be a strong desire to point out things that could make life much easier for the family. It is important and necessary to tread carefully. When first meeting the family, find out how they are feeling about aids and equipment. The ceiling track may be the fiftieth one a professional has recommended, but the very first for the family who has to adjust to this new reality and grow into this experience in order to accept it.

Be sensitive to what each piece of equipment might symbolize to a family. This will go a long way toward enabling the family to eventually recognize the need for the equipment and to agree to have it installed in their home. It will also help build trust between you and the family.

CHAPTER 33

Being in Our Home

Lurking somewhere in the back of my mind and underneath my heaped-up heart is the knowledge that there is absolutely no way we could care for our daughter at home without the help of a large team of caregivers. During the first year, we had very little help, perhaps 15 hours a week of daytime respite care. As time went on, Meredith's complexities became more obvious, and our need for in-home care grew. We live in a rural county where excellent support from developmental coordinators and case managers is available. They ensure that we receive the funding and in-home help to enable us to care for Meredith at home and to allow Tim and me to stay healthy as well.

The flip side of that gift is limited privacy. As strange as it felt in the beginning, we somehow adjusted to the routine of having people in our home on a regular, round-the-clock basis. If you are a professional who sees your clients in their home to provide respite, I address the following letter to you with love:

Dear _____ ,

(Enter name of night nurse/family relief worker here)

Welcome to our home! We are so relieved that you are here and that we will have a wee break from the unrelenting stress of a day in our life. Without your assistance and dedication, we would be unable to care for our child at home. We are especially indebted to you. This is not an exaggeration. We know that if we lost the support of the "village," we would have no choice but to have our daughter cared for outside our home. This would be devastating beyond our imagination.

Sometimes when you arrive, you might notice that I have aged ten years since you were last here. I have likely not had a full night of sleep in a week, and managing a shower today was as impossible as it is on many other days. I appreciate it when you ignore my appear-

ance. Cracking jokes about my Rod Stewart hairstyle will promptly get you on my bad side. Trust me! I saw my reflection in the mirror when I rose at 5:20 a.m. to relieve the last night nurse. I know what I look like in the morning. I am certain you assume that I spend my days and nights in my pyjamas. I actually do get dressed. You only see me in my night attire, at the end of a long day or first thing in the morning after I have just rolled out of bed.

I do my best to keep this house looking decent and welcoming out of respect for the fact that, technically, this is your workplace. I cannot imagine what it might be like to do my job in someone else's home. I appreciate that. I diligently clean the bathroom, wash the dishes and clean the floors so that you will feel comfortable while working here. You might have noticed that, some nights, the sink is full of dishes and the floor is not swept. Thank you for not letting me know that you noticed.

Although most employers prefer that their staff arrive a few minutes before their shift, we appreciate it when you arrive at the very start of your shift, and not a second earlier. You may be the fifth person to enter our home today, and between Tim's work schedule and the number of people who help with Meredith, we manage to be alone together each day for 30 minutes in the morning and 45 minutes in the evening, while our daughter is asleep. If you arrive early, I cannot predict what we may be doing during our alone time. We truly appreciate your understanding and your attention to this.

Before our daughter was born, Tim and I were private and even spontaneous people. Over the last decade, we have willingly sacrificed many things to make sure our daughter is cared for and content in her daily life. One of those sacrifices has been our privacy. Sleeping naked is a luxury of the past. Tim and I both know that, at any given moment, one of us will be woken up from our slumber to assist you. However, if I accidentally flash you as I make my way from the shower to our bedroom, unaware that you have arrived, forgive me. Please be assured that exposing my private parts to you is unintentional.

It took us a full year after our daughter was born to allow night nursing to be a part of our lives. We needed it and we were grateful for it, but truthfully, we never wanted it. To this day, a part of me has to shut down so that I can hand over my daughter to you, our nurse, and get the rest I need so I can make it through the following day. It is unnatural to have someone in your home at night to care for your child. Regardless of its necessity, this is one experience I will never be 100 per cent okay with. Ever. I hope you realize the immense trust I have in you.

When you come into our home, please respect the fact that, on some days, I may wish to chat about mundane things, yet on others, I may appear anti-social and off in my own world. Do not take this personally. My last few hours or days might not have gone as you imagine. I enjoy hearing about your life and family, but if I seem distant and bleary-eyed, stop talking. I am obviously too exhausted to engage.

If you are sick or think you may be getting sick, please understand that, although your absence means a sleepless night for us, your presence may result in one of us becoming sick. My husband and I cannot afford to be ill. We can't take time off from being parents or drop our daughter off at her grandparents' house if illness invades our bodies. Our daughter cannot afford to get sick. A common cold or flu can result in a hospital stay and could even be life-threatening. I know that you do not want to disappoint us, but we prefer that you take care of yourself and get well before returning to work.

If you have forgotten your lunch, please feel welcome to eat anything you find in our fridge or cupboards. We encourage you to use the kettle to make a cup of tea and adjust the thermostat to your comfort level. Make yourself at home and know that your job is more than a job to us. You are an essential part of our family, and we could not do this without you.

Love,
Meredith's family

CHAPTER 34

About Kids like Ours

When attempting to explain Meredith's complexities to medical teams or therapists who haven't met her, we often hear the phrase, "Oh, we deal with kids like her all the time." This puzzles me because we are also (often!) told that Meredith is extremely unique in her complexities. She has perplexed her doctors since day one, not following the usual pattern and un-expectedly doing things that other children with similar, complicated brain damage don't do.

When I first heard that phrase, especially from someone who had never actually met Meredith, it seemed to invalidate my concerns. It suggested that I should not waste another breath providing information about my daughter because they worked with and cared for "kids like Meredith" all of the time! As if it was old hat to them!

During a week-long stay at Roger Neilson House, our regional, pediatric, palliative care facility, I began chatting with a nurse at 4:00 a.m. I told her about how this phrase bothered me, even insulted me to a degree. She ex-plained that medical personnel use the phrase because they do in fact care for children similar to Meredith. In this facility, all children have medical fragil-ity; the majority are tube-fed, non-verbal and extremely dependent. She un-derstood that it could come across as flippant to parents or primary caregivers who have spent years figuring out the ins and outs of their child. To have your 24-hour care and extreme parenting reduced to "kids like yours" is a bit of a slap in the face, even if unintended. That conversation with the kind and pa-tient nurse, who sat and listened to the musings of a tired mother in the wee hours of the morning, has helped me to understand.

I've even caught myself saying, "Our friends have a child like Meredith." I cringe when I hear myself say that. It is not the phrase itself, because there are times when it's acceptable and not offensive. It boils down to the context in which it is being used. Using it to characterize the child you are speaking about ("a child like Meredith") basically tells the listener that the child has extraordinary needs and complexities. However, when it is used to undermine a parent's real concerns or to reassure a hesitant parent ("Don't worry, we deal with kids like her ALL of the time!"), it can come across as condescending, even when that's not the intention.

Now, when professionals seem overly confident and assume that my reluctance is simply a symptom of overprotectiveness, I give them the benefit of the doubt. I have been known to hand her over to those who find my uncertainties laughable, and who have apparently cared for "kids like Meredith" for years, and then walk away. I do not like doing this to Meredith, but to get my point across, drastic measures are sometimes required. It is usually only minutes before I am called back. Then they listen to what I tried to tell them earlier.

I still find the lack of trust in our intimate knowledge of Meredith to be one of the most challenging aspects of this parenting path. I am tired of trying to describe Meredith's complex idiosyncrasies and apparently never getting my point across. The listener may assume that, just because they have worked with children with disabilities in the past, they are automatically qualified to work with our daughter.

I recognize that it is also my responsibility, as Meredith's mother, to separate the physical and medical care from the emotional and psychological toll it can take on me. I have learned over time that expressing the need for extraordinary care for Meredith often falls on deaf ears, and that's okay. It isn't the job of every professional we encounter to lend a sympathetic ear to the ramblings of a sleep-deprived mother. It is the job of the professional, though, to sift through the ramblings, to hear and acknowledge what a parent is saying and trust that it is accurate and unlikely to be an over-dramatization. Approaching us with sensitivity and validating the knowledge we have about our own child will serve the relationship you have with the family.

As with most things, there is a balance to be found. The families of children with medical fragility must acknowledge and trust that the professional committed to working with "children like ours" day in and day out just might have some ideas and suggestions that will work and that may really help along the way. Having this insight, and openly discussing what each of us can offer, is the first step in building the trusting relationship that will best serve our child.

CHAPTER 35

Celebrating the Nurses
We Have Met Along the Way

I have always thought of nurses as celestial beings. My mother was a registered nurse. As a child, I saw nurses as professionals who magically dispelled pain, settled a crying baby, held the hand of a dying person and rubbed a back just right. I recall that my mother used to lay her special pins and nurse's cap on the kitchen table each evening, in anticipation of her early-morning shift. She always smelled good when she left in the morning and, by evening, she came home smelling like Band-Aids, rubbing alcohol and the Juicy Fruit gum that could always be found in her purse.

We have fond memories of the nurses who have cared not only for Meredith but also for us over the years. We have met and spent time with nurses at our children's hospital, and at Roger Neilson House. We have also spent time with nurses in our own community who take care of Meredith's medical needs, as well as the nurses who provide night nursing at our home so that my husband and I can get a decent night's sleep. My mother, who plays the role of nanny to Meredith, is also a blessing in our lives. She retired in February 2009, after 43 years of nursing service, though Meredith continues to keep her skills sharp!

Thirty-six hours after Meredith's birth, I was told that she would be given some formula through a nasogastric tube (a feeding tube that went in through her nose and down into her stomach). Since I was planning to breastfeed, I requested a breast pump. Two nurses took me to a private room and showed me how to use the pump. I was touched that the NICU nurses were so supportive of my efforts to breastfeed. It was perhaps partly thanks to these two nurses helping me get started immediately that I was able to feed Meredith breast milk for a full year.

Every evening, we dreaded the time when it got dark and we would pack up our things and say goodnight to our little girl yet again. Each time, we would find out who would be on shift for the night. We'd be so thankful and relieved when one of our favourite nurses would be caring for our baby until we returned in the morning. I slept best on those nights. Knowing that we could call the NICU at any hour of the night and have a nurse answer was so very comforting.

When I woke up to pump breast milk in the night, I would slip downstairs and call. A very calm and loving voice answered and never made me feel overly anxious. The nurses in the NICU were exceptional. It made all the difference. They took time to sit and talk with us as we worked through our worries and fears. They gave us some supportive contact, such as a pat on the back or a hug, when needed. They encouraged us to go for breaks and assured us that Meredith would be well cared for while we were gone. Most importantly, these nurses gave us hope when the future looked hopeless.

At only six weeks of age, Meredith was transferred to a nurse-monitored room on the fourth floor. We were sad to leave our NICU nurses, whom we had gotten to know and trust so much. Yet, we developed similar bonds with the nurses on this new ward. Nurses who choose to work with young patients and their families must possess unique and special qualities. Our nurses on the fourth floor not only cared for Meredith at night when we weren't there, they also counselled us, assisted us and taught us the skills we would need when we finally brought her home. With them, we learned how to change dressings, give tube feedings and administer medications through the G-tube. They constantly reassured us that they wouldn't send us home until we felt confident enough to do everything on our own. Their patience, sense of humour, genuine concern and guidance will never be forgotten.

At home, our night nurses provide care for Meredith so that we can sleep. Always acting professionally, they arrive with a relaxed and friendly attitude. As I have mentioned before, one of the hardest things to accept on this journey has been the tremendous amount of help needed to care for Meredith in our home. It is critical that those who work in our home recognize that they are not merely in a workplace, but in fact in our home. I fought against night nursing for as long as I could. I could not fathom having a nurse in our home every night. Yet, once we took the leap, we kicked ourselves for not doing it earlier.

I want the nurses who work with families of children with complex needs to know that they walk this path with us as counsellors, advisors, information providers and nurturers. This role is so very important and valuable to families like mine. Some of you on this path are present when we give birth or soon after. Some of you work at children's hospitals and rural community hospitals and will be with us throughout our children's lives, as we go through various surgeries, emergencies and illnesses. And some of you may be there at the end of our child's life.

Our journey, first as new parents and now as more experienced parents of a child with complex needs, would have been far more challenging and difficult had it not been for the nurses who quietly went about their day changing lives. Your presence, your words and your gestures can be empowering and can make stressful and traumatic times much more bearable. We are grateful to every nurse who has touched our lives. We cannot remember all of their names, but we remember ALL of their efforts in making this journey a little bit easier.

What I would tell you
. . . about preparing for the inevitable

CHAPTER 36

In the Shadows

I was raised in a home where birth and death were openly talked about and viewed as a normal and necessary part of life. From the time I was very young, we attended wakes and funerals because my parents taught us that it was the right thing to do and because my sisters and I often ended up singing in the church choir. I have never felt fear around death, and I don't back away from talking about it openly and being in its presence.

When Meredith was born, I felt Death lurking nearby and I knew that my time with her would be limited. Before we understood the depth of her brain injury and before her neurologist broke the news about life expectancy, we were aware that this beautiful child's life would likely not outlast our own. For the first few years this knowledge sat front and centre in our minds. If we ever allowed ourselves a moment to exhale and pretend our lives were as normal as everyone else's, reality would punch us in the gut with close calls and frantic rides to the hospital in the back of an ambulance.

In the days that followed each of these close calls, we would wander around in shock and horror at how quickly and abruptly things could change. I remember being hyper-aware of her smell and every sound she made. I would take countless photos of her, grateful for the opportunity to capture her through the lens of a camera. Should another close call occur without warning, at least I would have up-to-date pictures to remember her by.

I would have conversations with her and tell her that although I could not bear the thought of my arms without her in them, I understood if she needed to go. I always assured her that Tim and I loved her so much that if dying was something that had to happen, we would let her go. I don't know how much she understood, but these heartfelt conversations happened again and again each time I felt Death come near.

After we were referred to Roger Neilson House and Meredith was deemed palliative, I began to imagine scenarios of her death. What would it be like? How would it happen? Would it be sudden or lengthy? Would we be in the hospital or at Roger Neilson House?

I also contemplated how I would be afterward. I reasoned that since we have always known that we would likely outlive her, somehow I would be able to "handle" it okay. I remember speaking to my counselor about it shortly after we learned of Meredith's short life expectancy, how I matter-of-factly told her that I was more worried about Tim than I was about myself. I would be fine, I said. She looked at me and nodded, knowing that my denial of the enormity of what was to come was protecting me for now.

In the early days when things were excruciating for Meredith, I believed that death would come as a relief. Since there was no relief to be found, it was only natural that my weary mind would go to such lengths to imagine her having comfort and peace. I didn't want her to die, I just wanted her to have a break, and dying seemed to be the only way she would achieve that. Those days were like hell on earth, as I tried to navigate a road that had so many washouts, detours and sinkholes. I just didn't know how she (and we) could cope with it all day in and day out indefinitely.

Shortly after Meredith's tenth birthday, things changed drastically when one medication miraculously controlled the nocturnal seizures she had been dealing with for several years. For the first time in a decade, we were getting uninterrupted sleep. I remember keeping track as though they were gold stars on my chart of life. Look at us ... 93 nights of sleep in a row! Meredith's health stabilized and life got a little easier. Death seemed to retreat into the shadows, and we basked in this time knowing that it could reappear without warning.

We have had a good run. It's been almost four years since the first decade came to a close and life gradually got more predictable. Throughout this time, I have been very cognizant of the reality that this time is limited and our smooth sailing will change course eventually.

In June of 2016, we were heartbroken by the news that Meredith's scoliosis was progressing. At that time, we were told to come back in six months. Thankfully, six months later there was some change but not a lot, and we kept our fingers crossed that she might manage to get through puberty quickly, therefore reducing the impact of the scoliosis. At our most recent appointment, we were shocked to learn that again, the scoliosis is rapidly progressing and Meredith will be monitored closely over the next year. The options are slim when it comes to this common complication of her condition. We know that the next few years will likely see a decline in her health, and eventually the scoliosis may interfere with her organs and her body may begin to shut down. Corrective surgery is not an option for her, and so as we quietly anticipate the future, I feel Death emerge from the shadows.

I know that no amount of begging, negotiating or praying will chase Death away. It is a reality for everyone and everything that lives. For now, Meredith is oblivious to what is to come, and I choose to meet her where she is and accompany her along her life for as long as she has. I trust Death will keep a respectful distance until I have to let her go.

CHAPTER 37

Quality of Life vs Quantity of Life

When Meredith was born, our first triumph, aside from becoming parents, was the simple fact that she survived the first 48 hours after her birth. We had no idea that this would be the first of several moments where her life hung in the balance. The first couple of years were intense with uncontrollable retching, lack of sleep and relentless arching, a result of the cerebral palsy. In an attempt to reduce the retching and bring her comfort, we held her almost constantly except for when she slept during the night.

When she was around the age of two, she had a retching episode that was followed by something completely unexpected. It was as though she was in a trance. Her body stiffened so that her head was cranked to the right and her breathing became very shallow and inconsistent. She suddenly appeared lethargic, and so we called our nurse practitioner, who was watching over us and whose office was just around the corner. After arriving in record time, she listened to Meredith's heart rate and determined that we needed to call 911. She was taking only five breaths per minute. I rode in the ambulance and Tim followed in the car. The closest emergency room department was about 25 kilometres (15 miles) from our home, and yet it felt like the longest drive ever.

When we arrived she was assessed, and the acting physician called the Children's Hospital of Eastern Ontario (CHEO) for guidance on what should be done. Things get complicated when you are dealing with a child who has a significant brain injury. It was determined that continuing on to Ottawa by ambulance would be best. They sent a doctor, who stayed in the back with our girl while I sat in the front with the paramedic who expertly navigated the roads and traffic to CHEO. In the end, Meredith came out of this episode as seamlessly and unexpectedly as she went into it.

Not long after, we met with her neurologist, who told us point blank that Meredith's brain was misfiring. Somehow her brain was sending messages to her respiratory system to shut down and although she had managed to come out of that particular episode, she might not come out of a future episode. Her life expectancy was determined to be around seven or eight.

It was then that we were referred to Roger Nielson House. There we sat down with a palliative doctor and a nurse manager to create our first DNR (Do Not Resuscitate) form. There are many, many moments in this journey that I have forgotten, and then there are others that have been burned into my brain as though by the end of a branding iron. This was one of those branding moments. Having a tour of a hospice for children is an experience that no parent ever wants to have. It is a beautiful facility and we are grateful that it is a mere 120 kilometres (75 miles) from our home, but it is the last place we ever wanted to find ourselves.

This first experience with Meredith's brain misfiring jolted us into a reality we had, up until that point, pushed far away into those places where the darkest emotions reside. It was devastating to think that after all of the care and all of the love, and the sacrifice and the dedication, our daughter would most likely die before us. Each birthday came and went and although we celebrated another year, we silently grieved knowing we were one year closer to death. We didn't talk about it a whole lot. We didn't have to. Tim and I had an understanding that ran much deeper than words. In those early days, there were topics that were unspeakable – but we knew we were both experiencing the same pervasive thoughts, which interrupted morning commutes to work and made it impossible to peacefully drift off to sleep.

These episodes continued sporadically and seemingly randomly over the years. They always resulted in the same outcome. We would call 911 and quickly make our way to the ER department. Doctors would administer oxygen and monitor her until she came back to us. It was as though she had checked out for a little while, not sure if she wanted to stay or go, hovering between here and there. So far she has always come back to us. Each time we return home with gratitude knowing that it could have easily gone the other way.

When Meredith was around six years old, maybe the fifth time that this happened, the doctor in the ER asked us what we wanted to do if she went into cardiac arrest. We immediately responded with, "Do everything you can to save her." Whatever we had written on the DNR meant nothing to us. In that moment, we wanted her to live at any cost.

She didn't go into cardiac arrest, and we were sent home that night battered and shocked by how a normal evening had rapidly turned into an emergency. We stood out on our back deck under the stars with a bottle of wine and for the first time, we talked about the night she was born. We had found ourselves in survival mode after her birth, and we never took the time to talk about the night where everything as we knew it changed and our journey as parents began. This trip to the ER also prompted an honest discussion about what lengths we were prepared to go to in order to save her life and keep her with us. It was this difficult yet necessary conversation that had us questioning our desire to keep Meredith with us at any cost and the possible outcome of doing everything to save her.

Over the years, the DNR form has evolved. One would assume that the annual gatherings to update it would get easier, but they never do. Each update forces us to sort through the various scenarios that would warrant life-saving measures and the ones where it might be best to let nature take its course. We have struggled between our natural desire to save her at all costs and our natural desire to end any suffering and let her go.

There are no easy answers, and from my limited experience in mothering a palliative child, I think that we must rely on our intuition in these matters. I know that over the years of her life, my intuition has never led me astray when it comes to Meredith; and I have to believe that it will be equally reliable when it comes to her death. It is an emotional and psychological inner struggle of questioning whether or not we are doing the right thing by her. We fear that our selfishness in wanting more time with her will override common sense and compassion.

Making decisions concerning Meredith from a place of fear has never been our practice. We try to always come from a place of love, and although the fears swirl around my mind and threaten to overtake me, I keep them at bay. I always remind myself that since the beginning of her life, I have navigated this adventure (along with Tim) remarkably well. I know that we will navigate the ending of her life in the same way. We do our best to stay in the present moment and not allow our imaginings to take us too far ahead into the future. We consider others' input when needed but ultimately know that as her parents, we know better than anyone what is best for her.

In the end, it is about the quality of her life and not the quantity. I trust that we will know when it is time to let nature take its course.

CHAPTER 38

The Changing Tribe

The first time I attended the parent support group offered by our local pe-diatric hospice, I knew that the strangers surrounding me would become friends. I didn't know a lot about them personally but we shared a common thread of being parents to medically fragile children, and that would prove, over time, to be the glue that held all of us together. Up until that time, which was about seven years into this experience, Tim and I were very isolated and didn't know any other families who were travelling a similar path.

I remember feeling so relieved and connected after that first gathering. Here was a group of people who could open up their hearts and allow their deepest fears and worries to spill out onto the meeting room floor. There was safety in this space and a camaraderie that can only be shared by people who have gone through unthinkable experiences and emerged intact with an ability to still laugh and find joy in their lives. This was a group of parents with grit, resilience and unconditional love. I was both devastated and proud to be among them.

The truth is: I didn't want to be a part of this tribe. I hated that we had to endure a tour of a pediatric hospice. There were so many positive aspects of this place that would become a second home to many of my tribe members, but none of us wanted to be there. Being there meant that we had children we would likely outlive. And yet, if life turns out in a way you never imagined, having a tribe and a place like Roger Neilson House can be a game-changer and a life-saver.

When I first arrived in the group, I was one of the younger parents: that is, I wasn't necessarily younger than the other parents, but our daughter was younger. There were parents with children a few years older than Meredith, and I looked to them as though they were a beacon to guide me through a future that terrified me.

As time went on, the make-up of the tribe evolved. It could change very suddenly, without warning. One month, the group would gather as normal and the next month, there would be parents missing because their child was seriously ill and in hospital clinging to life – or worse, a child had died. Each time a child died, the future glared back at me as if to remind me that, in time, Tim and I would follow a similar path. Just when we felt we were getting a handle on things, we would have a close call or our friends would endure the death of their child, and we felt ourselves moving up in line.

There have been periods – after the first decade, when we were no longer struggling with the intensity and chaos of those early years – where I felt almost guilty attending parent group. I discovered, though, that my presence in the group was still valuable, because I was now the parent further down the road and could acknowledge and validate a newcomer's complex thoughts and raw emotions.

As I became busy in my career, I took some time away from the group, and to be honest I needed a break from this reality. As Meredith got her footing and we figured out how best to care for her while keeping things manageable, we retreated a little. It had been an intense decade.

Over time, the dynamics of the tribe evolve. Tim and I are the last remaining parents of that original group, as so many of our little ones have died. I am now considered an old mom, as Meredith is fourteen years old now. As we start to sense the beginning of major changes in the coming years, there are fewer parents to look up to. Most of our friends have transitioned from the parent support group to the bereavement group. We have not only grieved the loss of these beautiful children but have witnessed the deep suffering of their parents. We know that we, too, will walk that path at some point.

We walked together for a long time but reached forks in the road where we were forced to part ways. Those who have left are still in our view but walking a path far more treacherous and devastating than any they have known thus far. As I observe them from afar, I know that I, too, am kept under the watchful eye of the new moms in the group. They look to me and wonder how they will make it this far. All I can do is reassure them that I was once where they are now, and they will one day, perhaps, be where I am.

It is bittersweet to be an older parent. It means that Meredith has outlived the original life expectancy given to her. It means that I can now take what I have learned and hopefully comfort and reassure the new parents coming up the path behind me. It also means we are moving closer to that fork in the road. Since Meredith turned eight, each day has been an added bonus. We certainly didn't expect to have her with us this long, and so never take that for granted. We are also well aware that things are changing and this period of stability and predictability may soon come to an end. As I guide the newcomers, I also look to the ones who have gone before me – and I know that I, too, will continue on after the greatest loss of all.

CHAPTER 39

Plans and Practicalities

There are few people who are willing to speak about the inevitable outcome for all of us: death. It is one of very few guarantees in life, and yet we live in a culture that denies and hides from the fact that one day, we are all going to die. Speaking about the death of infants and children is counter-intuitive. We believe that children should not suffer or die, and yet they do because death is not selective as to when our time is up. The death of a child can result in complicated grief, because having to bury the child you gave life to, or parented through adoption or fostering, goes against our perception of the natural order of things. I use the terms "dead," "dying" and "death" as opposed to the phrases we have grown accustomed to – like "lost" and "passed away" – because our hesitation in using these actual terms perpetuates our denial about the inevitable.

My interest in the subject of death and dying started many years ago in high school when I was a student enrolled in a death education class. The teacher was way ahead of her time and bravely taught teenagers a taboo subject that most adults avoided. She even took the class on a field trip to the nearest city to have a tour of a funeral home. The school board threatened to fire her, but she persevered and ultimately continued to teach death education until her retirement. This course was extremely valuable to me, and it stayed with me more than any other class I attended in secondary school. I had even (briefly) considered a career in funeral direction; but life had other plans for me and I followed another path for many years, until life brought me back around to this end of the life cycle.

In late 2010, my maternal grandmother's health began to decline. She was in her 92nd year and it was obvious her body was starting to shut down. Her mind was sharp and she insisted that she still had lots to do and couldn't possibly be dying. But she was, and by Christmas, my mother – a retired nurse – and my father made a decision to bring her home to die. A room was set up, off the kitchen, with floor-to-ceiling windows which provided a view of the garden in winter.

On Boxing Day, an ambulance brought her home to spend her final days surrounded by familiar sounds and smells and the people who loved her most of all. Extended family and friends from the community came and went throughout the week to say a final goodbye to this matriarch. My sisters and I helped my mom care for her. I learned some valuable lessons in the days leading up to her death. I learned about the dying process and the things we were to watch for. My mom taught me the art of changing the sheets on an occupied bed. I also learned that dying is a lot like labouring and birthing.

I was intrigued by the similarities, especially in how we comfort a dying person. I used many of the same techniques I used to use when sitting with a labouring woman for countless hours. Things like having patience and cultivating calm and quiet. Creating an environment of dimmed lights, soft music, quiet or limited conversation. Giving gentle touch as reassurance, and using a warm or cool rice sock for comfort. It also included anticipating the needs, and doing all the intimate care, of a person who is preoccupied with the sacred task at hand. One thing I knew for certain was that I was partaking in a holy transition that would have a profound impact on my life.

On the night of January 1, 2011, we knew that death was near. Grandma's breathing had been laboured and the lucidity that was present had faded. There was a shift in the room, and I can only explain it as the same shift that I have sensed countless times just before the time of birth. Perhaps it is the lifting of a veil between this world and another. I am not sure what it is exactly, but it can be felt. I had returned home that evening to tend to Meredith, and by 10 p.m. I was being called to return to my parents' home, a mere 400 metres away, as Grandma was taking her last breaths. As I pulled into the driveway, I remember my mother standing in the doorway calling to me: "Hurry, she is still with us!" I joined other members of my family at the bedside in time to witness her last breath.

Immediately following her death, the community nurse was called to pronounce her dead. While we waited, we toasted her and sang some Irish songs, and just sat in the candlelight sharing stories and tears and laughter. After the nurse had come and gone, the funeral director arrived. He gently requested we leave the room so that he could place Grandma's body in the body bag and remove her from the home to the waiting hearse.

Although this is normal practice, it did not sit well with me, and in a very short time I was plagued by horrible thoughts of something similar happening to Meredith at the time of her death. I panicked to think of someone taking her body out of our home and having to sit there wondering where she was and how I would ever sleep knowing she was not in my care. Of course, my intellect stepped in and assured my worried heart that she would not be needing care by that time. But still the thoughts and worry around this transition in our lives left me searching for answers.

A couple of years after graduating as a Life-Cycle Celebrant, I met a friend for lunch who also happens to be a funeral director. Since I was still unsettled about aspects of my Grandma's death, I decided to ask what I thought was a bizarre question: Upon Meredith's death, assuming her death was expected and at home, could I go with her directly to the crematorium? I wanted to keep her with us until that time and then ride in the vehicle with the funeral people. She nodded her head "Yes," and I felt relief knowing that I would not lose all control, nor would I be forced to separate from her immediately upon her death. At this time, I wasn't sharing a lot of this with my husband, as I knew he was uncomfortable talking about death in general and we had yet to broach the topic of what to do after Meredith's life came to an end.

It wasn't until I completed a 300-hour course in community deathcare that I recognized we had far more options than I'd ever considered. With each new revelation, I would bring it up to Tim, and then drop the subject for some time. The more I learned, the more I reflected on my own end-of-life wishes and preferences, and conversations naturally unfolded between Tim and me. We began to have open discussions about where we would like to die (if given the option) and how we would like to be cared for afterward, including our wishes for our funerals and the disposition of our bodies. My training prompted me to think about death in a new way and to offer guidance to my family members.

I was comforted to know that in our province (and in most provinces and states) it is the law for families to care for their own loved ones after death. This means that a family member can act as the "funeral director." The majority of people are not aware that they can do all of the care of their loved one after death – including after-death care, the necessary paperwork, and transferring the body to the crematorium or cemetery. Most of us hire

154

the services of a funeral home to look after these tasks, although there is a growing movement of people who wish to return to the "old ways" of doing things. They may wish to have more power and control when it comes to caring for their family members not only as they die, but also following their death. In the 1970s there was a homebirth movement, and today there is a community deathcare movement.

My unexpected path into end-of-life care has been a blessing, as I cannot hide from the reality of death. I am surrounded by it on a regular basis as a funeral celebrant and as a teacher of a class I created on preparing for death. For five weeks, I lead a class of healthy mortals to understand all of their options and to come up with a solid plan for their own demise. The result is an ability to live life fully, knowing these details have been looked after. It is a gift to those you leave behind to have a clear idea as to your wishes. It isn't just about the practical things like funeral planning and wills. It also includes things like legacy letters, personalized eulogies and obituaries, and every other thing your family would need to know upon your death (your computer passwords, the magazines you subscribe to, the contact info of your closest friends, where your funeral plans have been made, etc.).

After preparing for our own deaths, Tim and I gradually began talking about Meredith and what we envisioned for her. This conversation did not happen in one sitting. There were topics (like home death versus hospice death) that needed time for processing and really wondering if this would be a good option. We disagreed about some things but were able to compromise. Surprisingly, speaking out loud about Meredith's eventual death deflated so much of the unspoken fear we had around it. We didn't realize how much it weighed upon us until we sat down and expressed in words how we imagined it would all unfold.

Talking about something so difficult will not hasten Death's arrival. It is a conversation that needs to happen if your child is medically fragile or deemed palliative. You will not be in the frame of mind to make such difficult decisions in the immediate aftermath of death, especially if the death is sudden. Talking this through and understanding all of the options available to you will make an unbearable time just a little more manageable. Leaving these big decisions until the inevitable has happened sets you up for unnecessary stress and extreme emotional vulnerability, both of which increase the likelihood of making decisions that you later regret.

Approach this delicate topic now with your spouse or close family members. If you are told that you should not be talking about it or that you are morbid for doing so, find someone else to speak with. Make an appointment with a funeral director to discuss options, and pre-plan some things if you are clear on what you will want for your child. If family-led death care and a home funeral appeals to you, research the laws in your province, state or country, and seek out the people who can assist you with this, such as death midwives, death doulas and home funeral guides.

You do not have to choose one or the other. Blended care is an option that involves your participation with the assistance of a funeral director. You may wish to spend time with your child after their death to touch them, wash their body, dress them and snuggle them one final time. These last rituals of caregiving can be soothing for a parent as they transition to a life faced without their child. It is perfectly acceptable to spend several hours or even days with your loved one after death before calling the funeral home. Of course, there are practical things that need to happen, but there is nothing wrong with allowing yourself time to determine when you are ready to let your loved one go.

Very early one morning, a couple of years ago, I received a text from a tribe mama. Her daughter had died at home. The palliative team had been involved and came to the home as needed. This mom let me know that her daughter had died seven hours earlier and the doctor told her to take as much time as she needed. Unsure what to do as morning approached, she reached out to me hoping I could offer some guidance. My advice was simple: "There is no rush. Snuggle in, sniff her neck, savour this moment. As her body goes through its natural process, you will intuitively know when it is time to let her go." She was afraid that she would forget her smell and how her body felt. I understood this fear as I have had it many times over the years. In these last moments, this fear carried an urgency for this mom. I shared with her that we can never remember exactly what it feels like, but we can recall that the feeling of it was divine.

Slowing down after death helps our psyche to understand what has occurred. It is not bizarre to spend time with your child (or any loved one) after their death if circumstances allow. Our culture has taught us to rush the process and tidy up as soon as possible. We generally have our loved ones buried within 72 hours after death. I truly believe this tendency to move forward so fast does much more harm than good.

Knowing what your rights are and what options exist, and having conversations with the people who can help you make it happen are all practical, proactive ways to prepare for the inevitable. It is one of the hardest conversations you will have, but it will also be one of the most freeing. It allows you to make your plans, tuck them away for the time being and get on with living. In the end, we must parent our children through death as we did through their lives: with deep respect and love, and by following our intuition <u>always</u>.

CHAPTER 40

Savouring This Moment

There are so many moments of parenting Meredith that I'd rather forget. Over the years, we have had close calls when time stood still. Together, we waited as our child's life hung in the balance. During those hours, we hovered between life and death, holding our breath to see if Meredith would breathe on her own again.

When told your child has a short life expectancy, you become acutely aware, intellectually, that your child will die ...... someday. You understand that you will likely outlive your child, yet that reality is unimaginable and feels completely unnatural and unacceptable.

In the days that followed a close call, I would become hyper-aware of every infinitesimal detail of our daughter's habits and behaviours throughout her day. I would suddenly take large numbers of photographs and catch every moment on video. These close calls were not-so-gentle reminders that there were no guarantees. Parents of children with medical fragility and short life expectancies live in a state of "knowing" – and yet, like all parents, we too get caught up in our day-to-day lives and can be taken by surprise as easily as anyone.

We often hear of those left behind after a death expressing the wish that they could have just "one more moment." If the death was unexpected, a sense of panic comes with the realization that this opportunity will never come to pass. In our day-to-day living, we tend to spend most of our time focused on the future. We arm ourselves with a list of daily tasks to be completed before we can lay our weary heads down to sleep.

Unless you are a Buddhist monk, it seems next to impossible to live in a state of full awareness every moment of the day. Sometimes, life presents experiences that force us to become acutely aware of how very precious one random and ordinary day can be. As parents of children with medical fragility, we are drawn to others like ourselves. Consequently, you will witness some of the parents in your circle coping with the deaths of their children. You will sit there thinking to yourself that, next time, this tremendous, life-altering loss could happen to you.

In the last two years, six children in our Roger Neilson House tribe have died. Some have succumbed to complications of their condition while others died suddenly. As a Life-Cycle Celebrant, I offer my services to my tribe as a gift to them. I want to ensure that their children are honoured with a meaningful ceremony that celebrates them as the unique people they were. Each child's death comes as a stark reminder that we, too, will be making this trek one day.

On February 29, 2012, friends of ours were devastated when their young son suddenly passed away. He was a child like Meredith who faced many challenges in his short life, both medically and otherwise. This young boy's passing made me acutely aware of how swiftly and abruptly it can all come to an end. The day following his death, I was standing at Meredith's bedside after giving her a bath. I buried my face in her warm neck and inhaled. I kissed her over and over as she made her happy cooing sounds. And then I wept. I wept for the parents of this little boy. I imagined how shocking these early days without him must be. This hit very close to home. I wondered, if Meredith was suddenly gone, how I would spend those "more moments" if given the chance. This is what I came up with:

> If I had more moments with you, Meredith, I would skip the morning dishes and scoop you out of bed in those early hours when you are still a bit groggy from your night-time medications. I would curl up on the couch with you in my arms and wrap us in the crochet blanket my mother made for me when I was a child. You are so very cuddly in the early morning, so I would take advantage of the lack of spasticity and I would hug you tight, kiss the top of your head, gaze into your eyes and stroke your cheeks. I would chat with you about all of the things we would do that day.

> If I had more moments, I would get a hold of your bare foot and sniff your toes while exclaiming, "Peee-uuuuu!!!" and pinching my nose. You would smile widely at my dramatic inspection. I would certainly shower you because I love to hear you giggle when I first spray warm water on your belly. I would not rush

and impatiently wrestle with you to achieve the goal of cleanliness. Instead, I would soap up your long legs, sing in the shower for you and take in all of your glorious, crooked body parts. Afterward, I would wrap you in your gigantic towel and tell you how much I love my little mermaid. I would take my time putting lotion all over you and I would carefully clip your fingernails and toenails. On second thought, I would skip the nail-clipping since you hate it so much. I would jiggle my body to imitate your shivering and you would smile back, knowing that I was playing with you.

If I had more moments, I would pay attention to the countless mundane tasks in our day, such as changing the dressing around your feeding tube for the 2,800th time (give or take a few times), and carefully comb your hair while watching you wiggle and arch from the sensation of the comb on your head. After you were dressed and ready, I would put my face up close to yours and tell you how pretty you are. Again, you would smile because you understand me even though words are not an option for you.

If I had more moments, I would not be in such a hurry for the family relief worker to arrive so that I could get busy with all of the things I need to accomplish in a day. I would cancel her shift so that we could hang out all day long, playing and giggling. Daddy would call in sick to work so that we could all be together without anyone else in our little world.

If I had more moments, checking email and Facebook would be unnecessary. Our time together would be so precious that I would not take one moment for granted. I would be conscious of every second and of everything you did. I would study your small hands, how they open and close like a sea anemone. I would examine your ears, eyelashes, lips and your little nose as if I were a scientist and you were under my microscope. I would sniff your neck and try so very hard to remember your smell because it is "your" smell, and I would know it even if you were lined up with 100 other children and I was blindfolded.

If I had more moments, we would read more stories and play repetitively with the toys that you love but that give me a headache after a while. We would also sit in silence, and I would listen to the sounds of your breath and the unique murmurings you make when you are content and sitting on the lap of someone you love. I would play the "I Love You" game over and over for as long as you kept smiling: I *(pointing to myself)* Love *(placing my hand over my heart)* You *(placing my hand on your chest)*! And then the reverse: And You *(pointing to you)* Love *(placing my hand over your heart)* Me *(placing my hand on my chest)*!

If I had more moments, instead of getting a load of laundry folded or supper started, I would lie beside you and read stories or blow bubbles. I would hold a mirror up in front of us and observe how perfect your skin is, while mine is really starting to show its age. I would watch your reaction when you see our reflections in the mirror side-by-side looking back at us.

If I had more moments, I would tell you all of the things that sit in my heart. Even if you were unable to understand all of my words, I would feel good knowing that I shared them with you. At the day's end, we would lay you on your futon and eat our dinner in your room while sitting on the floor. We would sing songs and play ridiculous games because your dad is the absolute best at making games fun. You would vibrate from overwhelming giddiness and soon it would be time to get ready for bed. I would make sure you had warm socks on and I would wrap you in a soft blanket and hold you until you started to nod off. Rather than putting you into your bed at your usual time, I might just sit there and hold you a little longer, if I had just a few more moments.

There are never enough moments to sustain us when we are forever separated by death from those we love and cherish. Even if by magic we were given just a little more time, it would never be enough.

What we do have is THIS moment, and if you are blessed enough to have your loved ones surrounding you, healthy or not, spend the day living as though it were your last day together. Remind yourself to savour the moments, for they are fleeting. When you find yourself laughing or smiling with your child, make the mental shift to focus and bring sharp awareness to that moment in time. Capture it in your mind's eye and memorize every detail so that one day in the future, when perhaps you are apart from your child or they have died, you will be able to close your eyes and "be there" – re-experiencing the feel of their skin, their smell, and the weight of their body in your arms. When we become consciously aware of those precise and idyllic moments and we step back to observe them, we are being fully present. All we have to savour is this moment, right now.

CHAPTER 41

One Day

One day, this life we live will cease to exist
and the future we dread will come to pass.
One day, my arms will be empty. Arms that held you from birth until death.
Every cell, every muscle, every tendon will recall
the weight of you in my arms.
One day, I will no longer hear the sound of your wheelchair
on the creaky hardwood floors nor the beeping of the feeding pump.
The silence will be deafening.

One day, there will be no need for night nurses and caregivers
and I will wait for the sound of the door to open but it never will.
One day, I will stubbornly have one foot in the land
of the living and one foot in the land of the dead.
I will refuse to let you go completely,
because to do so might be the end of me.

One day, I will sit in an empty house listening to the sound
of my breath and I will marvel that my body carries on
even though I am dead inside.
One day, my beating heart will be the only indication that I am still alive.
One day, I will have to relearn how to be in a world
that I left behind so long ago.
I will return to it kicking and screaming as the world I have known
for so long begins to fade into the past.

One day, I will be forced to relinquish my identity as your mother.
I will always be your mother but not in this time and place.
One day I will awkwardly answer the question, "Do you have kids?"
by stumbling over my words before blurting out,
"Yes, I once had a daughter."

One day, hopefully many, many, many days from now,
I will say a final goodbye to you, my darling Meredith.
One day, I will have no choice but to learn to live again.

What I would would tell you
. . . about my girl, Meredith

CHAPTER 42

And the Final Words go to Meredith

So many people look at you and see your limitations and your medical fragility. Some want to look, but turn away instead, because they don't want to appear rude. Others look for too long. To the majority of onlookers, you are a child with disabilities, a "poor little girl" in a "very sad situation."

Sometimes, I wish they could see what I see. I don't blame them for the fact that they can't, because before I got to know you, all I saw was a sick and disabled baby. I could barely see anything else through my angry tears. As time passed, my grand wishes for you dwindled until the only thing that really mattered was that you lived one more day. That was all. The dreams I once had for you – and held onto despite what our seasoned neurologist predicted – would be nothing short of miracles: walking, talking and eating. But all those dreams slipped away over the months and years that have passed.

As the dreams and yearnings evaporated, something even more magical replaced them. By letting go of the things I wished you could do and be, I made room for seeing you as you are. As you grew, so did my ideas of how things should be. In fact, after some time, the word "should" no longer had a place in my vocabulary. Eventually, I no longer compared you to others because I finally saw you for who you are.

I have had the privilege of seeing past the things that everyone else can't help but see. What I see is your brilliance, which cannot be dimmed by a brain that functions differently than was intended. Through your eyes, I connect with your spirit, and I know that you understand so much more than we realize. You may be trapped in your body, unable to run, dance, skip or twirl, but when I hold you in my arms and you look into my eyes, I see YOU – your essence, your pureness, and that magnificent light embodied in each of us.

I no longer have the expectations I used to have. Tim and I have learned to let go, to no longer be burdened by developmental milestones, shattered dreams, or broken hearts. My only wish now is that everyone else could see you as I do.

THE ORIGINAL BLOG *(Unedited)*

December 11, 2003

Meredith has made huge progress since she arrived at the Children's Hospital of Eastern Ontario (CHEO) almost a week ago. We were able to hold her for the first time yesterday, a momentous occasion that was delayed. She has been taken off of most medication and today we hope she will be drug-free. She is out of the incubator, so we can touch her, smell her and kiss her. Today we look forward to seeing her without the respirator tube in her nose and if all goes well, we will give Meredith her first bath and hair washing. Yesterday, Meredith underwent her first MRI. The results showed some trauma in the last seconds before delivery. They can't tell us much yet but we know that the three of us will have many challenges to overcome in the weeks, months, and even years to come. Further testing and another MRI will be done in the next six to eight weeks. We'll know more then. For now, we're focused on bringing Meredith home so we can pick up where we left off on December 5. We pray that Meredith learns to breathe on her own and is able to breastfeed, suck, and swallow as this will guarantee her pass out of CHEO.

This time would be unbearable without the love and support of our family, friends, and all of those who we don't know personally but who are also praying for Meredith.

Thursday, December 11, 2003   EVENING UPDATE

Wow! What an incredible day we have had! Yesterday was extremely rough with the MRI and the realities of what we may face in the future, but today Tim walked in to find a sleeping Meredith. She was out of her incubator and resting with her pink bunny. I arrived about an hour after Tim. I had to wrestle her out of Tim's arms so I could have a turn! We sang to her and talked with her and she stretched and yawned and made those beautiful cooing sounds that newborns make. The big tube was out of her nose and we could see her whole face for the first time. I kissed her head and hands and chubby arms and she opened her eyes and stared at us as if to say, "I know your voices but who are you exactly?" She is being fed through a tiny tube that goes into her nose and the nurse puts a drop of my milk into her mouth so that she can have a taste. Then she puts some on a piece of gauze and places it near her nose so she can smell it. Tomorrow we will put her skin-to-skin and let her snuggle and nuzzle my breast in preparation for future breastfeeding. She is showing signs of gagging and swallowing activity, which is all very positive.

Tim is over the moon with his little girl. He beams from ear to ear while holding her in his big, strong arms. Today was wonderful! We are on cloud nine tonight and can't wait to go back tomorrow. We will hopefully be bathing her. We didn't want to put her through too much today.

Friday, December 12, 2003   MEREDITH IS ONE WEEK OLD

It is 5:23 p.m. as I type this and at this time one week ago today, I was working hard at pushing Meredith out of my body. At 7:23 p.m. she finally emerged and I was so joyful to have completed this momentous task. Events went extremely opposite to what we had dreamed and planned immediately following her birth. Our "firsts" with Meredith have been delayed.

The tubes have been taken out of her belly button and now there is just an IV in her heel. She is more beautiful today than she was yesterday. I decided to check out her sucking reflex and our midwife suggested I put my baby finger in her mouth. She wasn't sure at first but after a few attempts she started sucking my finger vigorously! Before we left, our nurse placed drops of my milk on Meredith's lips and she lapped it up like a kitten. She was very alert today. She focused on us and followed our voices. So today was an awesome day and we hated to leave her especially because she seems to look at us while we're packing up. No bath today but planning on it tomorrow.

Saturday, December 13, 2003

We arrived this morning at 10 a.m. to find Meredith lying wide awake in her bed. Our nurse told us that she had a great night and fed from a bottle! We are holding off on initiating breastfeeding until she can master the sucking reflex so she won't be overwhelmed by my let-down. If she choked we would be dealing with a major setback. It is painful for me to stick a bottle in her mouth. I always looked forward to breastfeeding. She was far more vocal today. Trying hard to cry but we think she startles herself when she makes any noise. It won't be long though before we hear her wail.

Meredith finally had her first bath today! She enjoyed it thoroughly. Tim bathed her with the guidance of our nurse, Theo. He did a great job and Meredith loved every moment. Her hair was washed and she had a sponge bath. Her father was so gentle and took his time to clean out every crease. Meredith was exhausted from this new experience so she spent the next couple of hours sleeping in her daddy's arms. When it was time to feed her again, I held her skin-to-skin and then attempted to feed her from a bottle. It went fairly well. Meredith burped and sputtered, but managed to get some of it down. The rest of the feeding was through the tube. I held her and sang to her while her belly was filled. She looked at me steadily. We have fallen in love. We have had another positive day. We are so happy and in love with our baby. Our nurse said she is already doing things the neurologist thought she might never do. In only 48 hours after we were told she may never be able to use her mouth for swallowing and eating, she is taking a bottle. We just might prove them all wrong! Meredith gained 200 gm since yesterday. She now weighs 8 lb. 6 oz. It's looking like Daddy's heart belongs to Meredith now. We thought we knew what love was. Little did we know.

Sunday, December 14, 2003

We spent a calm, relaxing, and fairly uneventful day with Meredith. Well, of course, she had her accomplishments. She took breast milk by bottle again. I requested a bigger nipple as I felt that if she was ever to breastfeed she needed to have a bigger nipple that didn't pour milk into her mouth. Sure enough it worked and she took a lot more than yesterday. By Tuesday she will be up to her full amount of milk if all continues to go well. In the meantime, we snuggle skin-to-skin while she feeds and we try to connect her full belly to my breast. I sneak her some drops orally too!

Meredith had visits today from our second midwife as well as both sets of grandparents. Visits are being kept to a bare minimum as there is a respiratory virus going around that adults can carry and is easily passed to fragile babes. Hopefully, we'll have her home soon enough. Our nurse commented on the amount of love and support that Meredith is receiving. She said that some parents don't come in at all. She also said that it has been medically proven that love and prayer makes a big difference in making miracles happen. We didn't need medicine to prove that to us.

Meredith isn't out of the woods yet. We will continue to make our journey to CHEO each morning and shower our babe with kisses, strokes and touches.

Monday, December 15, 2003

We are exhausted after a long day at the hospital. I managed to get a parent's room for a couple of hours to sleep so that we could stay past 3 p.m. We usually try to avoid the rush hour traffic. Today we left at 6 p.m. and had to run a few errands, getting us home at 7:45 p.m. A very long day. Thankfully, my sister Stephanie had dinner ready and waiting for us when we got home.

Meredith seemed less active today. She had been awake earlier in the morning so when we arrived she was starting to nod off. The day was hectic in our room and it was very noisy. I attempted to give her some milk out of a bottle at her noon feeding, but the stress of all of the racket and chaos caused both of us distress, and within minutes I was in tears wanting to throw the bottle out the window. I didn't, but I sure felt like it. It is hard to be patient with this part of this journey. I wonder if we'll ever get to the breastfeeding part.

After a sleep and some food I returned for her 3 p.m. feeding ready to try again. The occupational therapist (OT) came by to assist and was very pleased with Meredith's sucking abilities. Meredith kicked into high gear and gulped down more than double the amount of milk she previously was able to drink, though she did cough a little. We stopped there and did the rest of the feeding by tube, as we didn't want to overwhelm her. We were so proud of her. Tomorrow, the OT will visit us and we'll try it all again.

Since I am not breastfeeding, Tim and I are sharing the other duties so that we can participate equally in her care. Tomorrow I will bathe her. It is harder and harder for me to leave her each day. Hopefully, we won't have to leave her much longer. We want to have her home. I am starting to feel a little worn out.

Thursday Morning, December 18, 2003

We are taking a few days to gather strength and are coming home from the hospital a little earlier in the day because exhaustion was becoming a serious problem. The stress of this is starting to take its toll, but we are doing our best to pace ourselves and address each hurdle as it arises.

Meredith has also had a rough couple of days. She started taking her full feedings and tolerated the first few well, but on Tuesday night she started spitting up her feedings and was taken for tests yesterday afternoon to determine the cause. We will find out the results this morning. Meredith cried, truly wailed, for the first time Tuesday morning. Tim and I were thrilled. We had waited 11 days to hear our baby cry. She was kicking her legs and crying while Tim was trying to change her. I bathed her the same afternoon and she squealed through the hair washing portion. What joy to do such a simple task with our baby.

Afterwards, we met with the neurologist and he brought us down a few notches from the high we were on. He discussed the realities of Meredith's future. There had been some improvement on Friday's EEG compared to the one done three days following her birth. They weren't seeing seizure activity anymore, but there was still the potential for seizures. Some positive news, I guess.

It is very tough though. Going to CHEO each day is pretty depressing. The energy is heavy as we are surrounded by shocked parents and sick babies. The nurses and staff have been great for the most part and that helps a lot. We are experiencing a mix of emotions and are just trying to get through each day.

This has been the hardest introduction to parenthood. Seeing your baby suffer and struggle so much in the first two weeks of life is almost unbearable. This is by far the most joyful and yet the darkest time of our lives. It is so comforting to know that we are in the thoughts of many people. It makes this experience far less isolating.

Thursday Evening, December 18, 2003

Did I mention that we are on an emotional roller coaster? This morning was hard. Tim was up early unable to sleep waiting for today's news about Meredith's tests. I had a restful evening last night and a good night's sleep so I was feeling stronger this morning. I had a good, supportive chat with my parents by phone before getting organized for another day at the hospital. The roads were treacherous. I ended up calling the hospital to say we might not make it to hear the news. It took us an hour and a half to drive from Carleton Place to CHEO.

Lo and behold, we made it just in time to hear the latest updates on Meredith. It turns out her esophagus is not working as well as it should be. This is common and usually corrects itself in time. But because Meredith has neurological problems they're not sure if the two are connected. So now our baby girl will be tube fed through her nose for the next four to six months (yes, months!) before they reassess. They have told us that we may be able to bring her home in the next couple of weeks. We will be spending Christmas at the hospital this year with our baby girl. We need to be trained in tube feeding and they will only let us take her home if we're confident in feeding her and they're confident that we can manage this essential task. Sadly, Tim may be back at work by the time we have her home.

The occupational therapist told me that I will not be breastfeeding. After helping countless new moms' breastfeed their babies it was sad to hear but it is a small sacrifice at this point. This is a unique situation. If, at any point I can breastfeed, I definitely will. Right now, Meredith is at risk for aspirating and so tube feeding will be her only way to get my breast milk safely at this time. The OT was very upset when she watched the test being done, as she said Meredith has a great suck. She can breathe and she can swallow, but she can't do all three at once with her weak esophagus. We pray that it heals because if it doesn't Meredith will have to be tube fed for the rest of her life possibly. This is something that we don't even want to imagine at this time.

After this initial shock we had to leave the room again as Meredith was having her third EEG since birth. After some tears and a phone conversation with my sister, I joined Tim, and Tim's sister, Sherry, with Meredith. The EEG was over and Meredith needed to be bathed. Oh, how we love to see her naked, pink body, and to wash that luscious hair. She had her first full bath today as opposed to a sponge bath. She didn't mind at all. She squawked a bit at first but then relaxed and looked around. We got her cozy in her nightie and spent the rest of our time with her in our arms. The day seemed short with all of the interruptions and activities. We left at our usual 3 p.m. time, as Tim was exhausted from the little sleep he had had the night before and I need to rest. Tonight, we will relax and try to find an exterminator for the squirrels who have taken up residence in our ceiling upstairs. Just what we need!

Friday, December 19, 2003

Happy birthday to Meredith who is two weeks old today! We celebrate anything at this point. It was a fairly uneventful day today. I am feeling angrier these days than anything. I guess it is normal when one is in a crisis situation. It's the little things, like the constant beeping of machines, sad parents and sick babies, a feeling of being watched, lack of privacy with your baby, and so on. We sometimes feel we are not parents yet. We know we are Meredith's mom and dad, but there is some disconnection, as we are not her primary caregivers just yet. This is so tough. I know that there is a very primal force at work here too, which turns me into a Mother Bear when anyone says anything negative, or someone tries to be humorous and well, they're just not that funny. Thank God for our sense of humour. One day at a time.

We are so grateful for all of the care and support, and offers of food, rest stops, and anything else we might need. We know right now that we will never be able to thank everyone enough for all of the love we have received over the last two weeks. I have been told that prayers are being said for Meredith around the world, in Ethiopia, Australia, the U.S., South Africa, Cuba, Nicaragua, Southeast Asia, and the U.K.

Not much to report today. Meredith spit up after a few of her feedings, but rested most of the day in our arms. She was very active and fussy, but we loved hearing her make all of those noises, and feel her squirming around. Now it's time to eat the dinner that my sister prepared for us and relax a bit before heading to bed. Another day at CHEO awaits.

Sunday Morning, December 21, 2003

We got home late last night so here is the update from yesterday. Not much to report except for the usual things like the awesomeness of a yawn, a sneeze, a cry. You know…the things that parents swoon about when their very own creation performs these normal, everyday actions.

When we arrived yesterday morning there was a wrapped Christmas present in Meredith's crib, as well as a Polaroid picture of Santa Claus standing next to her bed Friday night. Very cute! Five NHL hockey players came to the hospital to visit the children and babies spending Christmas in the hospital. They gave out autographed cards and when they offered to have a picture taken with Meredith, Tim declined, as she was sleeping peacefully in his arms and he didn't want to disturb her.

Yesterday, my younger brother arrived home for the holidays from Waterloo and stopped in to meet his newest niece for the first time.

Monday Morning, December 22, 2003

We had a rough day emotionally yesterday so I chose not to write. We are riding the waves of this experience as best we can. We don't have a choice right now but to be brave, courageous, and hopeful in the face of death (not an issue now), challenges, fears, worries, illness and the unknown. We have never known a love so fierce and strong as the love we have for Meredith. Some days we take it one day at a time and other days we take it one moment at a time. Just when I think I cannot cry another tear, I get a break from the grief and manage to have some breathing space to rejuvenate and gather my strength to face another day. We are not exceptionally, brave souls but simply parents who have been introduced to motherhood and fatherhood in a way that we never would have imagined. We know in our hearts that this crisis time will eventually pass and that life will return to "normal" although it will be a new normal to the one we once knew. Isn't it that way for everyone who has a child?

The biggest stress we face is watching our baby girl suffer. Yesterday, she cried and fussed most of the day with gas pains due to the air getting into the tube. We are not to rock, burp, pat or move her. Our biggest challenge is fighting every natural instinct to comfort our child. Finally at the end of the day we said, "Screw this!" We thought the loss of milk from spitting up was far less important than giving her some comfort. It was heartbreaking to be there yesterday.

Rest assured, we are not in denial about our feelings, nor are we super human. We are just two parents coping with the most magnificent experience of our lives.

Monday Evening, December 22, 2003

We arrived this morning and Meredith was not in her usual spot. Even her crib was missing! She had been moved to another room because they are short staffed over the holidays. The new room is crowded–seven babies with their parents and nurses. No chance for skin-to-skin contact in this room, as there is no room for a screen that provides some privacy. We found Meredith in the arms of Al, her day nurse. We were told that although she lost 25 grams last night, she managed to keep her milk down since yesterday morning. What a relief for us. She was quite calm today and as a result we were less stressed. We rocked her and patted her back, and she slept happily all afternoon.

We met with a social worker from the Children's Treatment Centre who talked to us about the range of services offered should Meredith require extra care. It is highly likely that she will. She told us about a baby who was born without part of his brain. His prognosis was grim as you can imagine, but lo and behold, this child can do everything. The rest of his brain compensated for the part that was missing. The doctors are still puzzled. There is so much that they don't know about the human brain. We were relieved to know that Lanark County has programs in place so we won't have to drive too far for every appointment. For things that aren't offered in our immediate area, there is an office about 40 minutes away that we could go to. I hope we never have to go there though, but it is comforting to learn that there is lots of support for us and Meredith if needed.

I cried a lot today and feel much better now. It's funny that when you release the tears and vent to a caring, sympathetic ear the world seems brighter. Anyway, we're home now with our sense of humour intact and supper in the oven. Tomorrow is another day.

Tuesday, December 23, 2003
What a great day! I went to the hospital solo today. Tim stayed home for a much needed "me" day as well as a break from the hospital. I arrived to the room Meredith had been moved into yesterday and she wasn't in her spot. I asked the nurse and she said she had been moved back to room #1. I went to room #1 and they said she wasn't there either. I found it amusing imagining that Meredith decided enough was enough and escaped the hospital. I returned to room #2 and there was Meredith sleeping in the corner on the opposite side to where she was yesterday. Her nurse came in soon afterward and apologized for the confusion.

Meredith awoke when I arrived at her bedside. I was told that she had kept all of her feedings down overnight and had gained a whopping 95 grams. I was thrilled and I knew her father would be too.

My dad arrived, and our nurse arranged for us to have three hours in a room known as "the cuddle corner" (CC room). It is a cozy room with a couch, dim lights, television, a sink and breast pump. I was thrilled. It was a step closer to feeling closer to home. My sister arrived and joined me after dad headed out. It was wonderful to have privacy and peace and quiet. The floor was a zoo again today, and I was so grateful to have this small corner to sit with Meredith and have lunch. Our doula, Tammy, came by around 1 p.m. to visit. We hadn't seen her since the morning after Meredith was born. It was good for us to reunite.

We returned Meredith to her room at 2:45 p.m. and then headed home. It was an amazing day. Tomorrow morning is Meredith's milk study test, and our nurse from today is on again tomorrow. She is a gem. She said she would arrange to get us a room for the afternoon.

Wednesday, December 24, 2003   CHRISTMAS EVE DAY

We won't be home tonight. We plan to spend the day with Meredith, have dinner with Tim's sister and her family in Ottawa, return to the hospital and then sleep at Tim's sister's place so that we can spend Christmas morning with family while close to Meredith.

I know that miracles do happen in this world and that we must believe that there are many in store for Meredith now and in the weeks, months, and years ahead. Conceiving Meredith, growing her, and giving birth to her were all miracles. These miracles we often take for granted because people do them every day. I have not taken for granted the miracle of creating life and bringing her into this world only a mere two and a half weeks ago.

Thursday, December 25, 2003   CHRISTMAS DAY

We spent yesterday with Meredith, and then had a wonderful Christmas Eve with Tim's sister's family. We were in bed by 10 p.m. (very late night for us!) and up by 7 a.m. today. We were on our way to the hospital by 9:15 a.m. to spend the day with Meredith. We wheeled Meredith's crib to the CC room. Santa Claus arrived to the Neonatal Intensive Care Unit (NICU) by mid-morning, and he brought Meredith and the other babes a special CHEO Teddy Bear. She didn't seem too impressed but we were!

The rest of the day was spent quietly gazing at our miracle. We read her stories, sang Christmas songs and I got my skin-to-skin fix. We bathed her in the afternoon, which ended up being a battle of wills. She didn't mind the hair washing part but hated the sponge bath. We cleaned her up fast…Tim took the right side and I took the left. Soon her hair was fluffed up and she was cozy in her nightie. She rested in her daddy's arms while I changed the bedding on her crib. We had great intentions of having a family photo taken today with Meredith wearing her red velvet sleeper, but she was irritated when I tried to dress her so we only snapped one picture.

It was a wonderful day. Tim and I had lots of nice chats and soothing cuddles with Meredith. We had lunch and opened gifts, listened to classical music, relaxed and counted our blessings. That Cuddle Corner is going to save us, I swear. One of my former clients whose baby spent a month at CHEO dropped in to bring the nurses some treats. It was great to see her and her husband and their baby who I hadn't seen in four months. It was also reassuring and comforting to chat with them, as they were in a similar boat as we are now not that long ago…grim predictions of the future, unknowns and worries. It gave us another boost of hope.

Saturday, December 27, 2003

We spent yesterday and today with Meredith and she is now on continuous feedings, as they felt her reflux problem was causing her a lot of pain. She slept peacefully on Wednesday and Thursday, and was a new baby on Friday. She was simply miserable and it was very hard for us to see her in pain. Today though, she was calm and happy. We spent the day in the Cuddle Corner once again. Last night Meredith gained 115 grams!!

There are a few things that we feel a need to clarify. There have been "rumblings" of incorrect information floating around regarding what exactly happened on December 5 to bring us to this place where we have found ourselves. As most of you know, I have attended births for the last five years as a doula, and after attending close to 100 (90 per cent in hospital), I gained a lot of invaluable knowledge and experience. When the time came for Tim and I to plan our birth we chose midwives as our primary caregivers and planned a home birth. This decision was not made in passing and we felt that our home was the safest and most comfortable place for us to bring our child into the world.

This was an educated and an informed decision. Our primary midwife is the most experienced and knowledgeable caregiver I have ever encountered in my career as a doula. Since she had attended more than 2,000 births in countries all over the world, we had, and continue to have, complete faith in her abilities. What happened at Meredith's birth had absolutely nothing to do with our choice to give birth at home. Although we didn't need to be told, we were assured by several doctors that the same outcome would have occurred had we chosen a hospital delivery.

Meredith experienced hypoxia, a lack of oxygen content in the tissues. They do not know why it happens and therefore cannot prevent it from happening. The neurologist said he could tell from the MRI that it occurred in the minutes before Meredith delivered. It can also occur throughout labour, but this was not the case for us. Meredith's heart rate was normal throughout labour and there were never any signs of distress. The midwives had the appropriate equipment, electric suctioning, as well as oxygen, ready and waiting, and used it immediately to help Meredith along. The possible outcome for

Meredith happens in about two in every 1,000 births. Time will tell how well the rest of her brain compensates and the healing that will take place.

In situations like ours, it is sometimes easier to focus on why situations occurred, easier for people to try to find answers as to why something like this could have happened. It is easier to cope with tragedy when someone or something is to blame. There is no clear reason why this happened and there is no one to blame. The same outcome would have occurred had we delivered in the hospital with an obstetrician. It would have occurred even if we delivered on the floor at CHEO. It is my wish that those of you who are trying to explain why this situation has happened will eventually accept that sometimes things just happen and there is no one or nothing to blame. If we could birth Meredith over again we would still choose the caregivers we chose, and we would not change one minute of the labour, the birth experience or the location.

Tim and I have been given Meredith and we love her. We cannot look at things as though there was a mistake, as that would insinuate that Meredith was somehow flawed. We think she is perfect the way she is. Meredith has a lot to teach us about love, life, acceptance, strength and courage.

Sunday, December 28, 2003
We arrived at CHEO at 9:30 a.m. to baby Meredith snoozing. We booked the large parenting room, exited the NICU and wheeled Meredith down the hall to our new haven. Meredith still seemed a little snuffly from the cold she was getting yesterday, but she was peaceful and comfortable. As soon as we entered the room she started crying. I picked her up and calmed her, and then placed her in Tim's arms who had found a nice, cozy chair to recline in. Meredith was wide awake and alert. We had never seen her so alert. She gazed at Tim. He sang to her exaggerating his mouth movements as he spoke. She stared at him intently, and soon her mouth was moving with his. It was so funny. It was as though she was mimicking him. This went on for about an hour and a half. Meredith was so focused on Tim's face and when I went over and spoke to her, her eyes shifted to my face. It was amazing.

By 11:30 a.m., they were both asleep in the chair, exhausted from their playtime. Soon I took over holding Meredith so that Tim could get a bite to eat. She was so calm and cuddly. Tim pulled the sofa bed out and had a good nap along with Meredith. I read my book and just sat there feeling so at

179

peace and joyful in this moment. Watching my husband and baby resting was simply wonderful. Meredith kept stretching and touching my face with her fingers. It was a relief to see her so happy and comfortable.

It was bath day and Meredith was not at all pleased with having to be washed. I quickly got her dressed and wrapped up and back into Daddy's arms.

Not much to report these days. The most commonly used phrases at CHEO are: "Time will tell," "Wait and see," and "You just have to take it one day at a time." So until time passes and we have waited patiently our updates will be fairly standard baby talk.

Monday, December 29, 2003

Another day at CHEO under our belt. We arrived and both parenting rooms were booked! Arrrgghhhhh! Tim and I reasoned that we were fortunate for the past few days and so we could handle one day in the regular room. We found out very quickly that in fact I couldn't handle the usual room well after all. I was shedding tears within minutes, as one of the babes was crying and Meredith was fidgeting. I couldn't sing to her as there was so much activity. I also thought that other mothers and babes might not want to hear me singing. And then an angel in the form of a young mother whose baby was born prematurely appeared. She had booked one of the rooms for the day but had just heard that she could take her baby to her room at the motel on the CHEO campus for out-of-town parents. She kindly offered us her booked room. Thank God for small blessings.

We quickly moved ourselves out and settled into the Cuddle Corner. Meredith had a fussy night we were told, but was now sleeping soundly in our arms. Our incredible nurse, Jeannie, seemed to think that her nights and days were mixed up. So we relaxed for the next few hours and in no time it was almost 3 p.m., and time to head back to the room and get ready to leave.

Just before we left, Jeannie shared with us that the surgeons were looking for OR time for Meredith. They are anticipating that Meredith will need a gastrostomy tube ("G-tube"). This is a tube that would be put into Meredith's tummy and that would be the way she would be fed. My heart sank. Imagine, our baby girl needing surgery after everything she has already been through. This isn't necessarily permanent and might mean we can bring her home sooner than later. We hate having to trust that these recommendations are the best solutions. I have never been the biggest fan of allopathic medicine and so I am doing my best to ask questions, proceed with caution and trust to some degree that Meredith is in the best care.

I am taking tomorrow off from CHEO. I will miss my daily fix of Meredith but will also enjoy staying home for a day away from the hospital. Tim will be on his own to deal with fussy moments and Meredith's feistiness. A consult with the surgeons is planned for Wednesday. Our adventure continues...

Wednesday, December 31, 2003

The last day of 2003 is coming to a close. A new year will begin in a mere seven and a half hours.

Today was tough. I was dreading going in. I knew we would be meeting with the doctor to discuss the G-tube. When we arrived we managed to get the parenting room. Just as we were wheeling Meredith towards the door of the room a man appeared to say he had the room reserved until 2 p.m. With an obvious breakdown of communication somewhere we returned to the NICU and thankfully got the Cuddle Corner instead. Meredith was fussy when we arrived and I knew reflux was bothering her. She was arching her back to alleviate the gas. Tim held her and she settled down in no time. Our day was spent like the other days–holding Meredith in our arms, gazing at her, and smiling at all of her movements, yawns, coos and breaths. What a beautiful baby we have created. We are so proud of our baby girl.

Then the doctor on-call for the next three weeks arrived along with the nurse manager to talk about the G-tube surgery. They want to insert a G-tube, as well as do another procedure called a fundoplication, which involves folding the top of the stomach around the bottom of the esophagus to tighten it to prevent reflux. She then told us that from what she could see from the chart Meredith would likely need a G-tube for the rest of her life.

She asked what we knew about Meredith's prognosis. We recited what the neurologist had told us. She read more notes and gave us a grim prediction of what Meredith's life would look like. I was devastated once again and wanted to scream and run out the door. Instead I calmly asked questions and was told to live in the present, and that although some kids do surprise, we should prepare for the severe disabilities that Meredith would most likely live with.

On the ride home, I cried and cried and cried. Tim reasoned that she wasn't a neurologist and we should therefore take her words with a grain of salt. We will arrange to meet with the neurologist next week again and have him examine Meredith. It has been about a week and a half since he last saw her. *God, grant me the serenity to accept the things I cannot change, the courage to change the things I can and the wisdom to know the difference.*

After shedding my tears and frustrations, I feel peace again. Tim and I will continue to do what we have been doing all along. We will love Meredith today as she is and we will continue to hope for a miracle while always knowing that our baby girl will likely face a challenging life ahead. This is an incredibly emotional roller coaster. We can go either way. We can give up, throw in the towel and put in time until grim predictions become a reality, or we can live each day positively while helping Meredith to reach her full potential, whatever that may be.

Saturday, January 3, 2004
Wednesday's entry was not intended to sound like a doctor bashing fest. I have heard from others about similar experiences. We do understand that doctors cannot become emotionally involved with their patients and their families. They would likely go completely insane if they were to do that. It is frustrating and I admit, I absolutely hate having to meet with them, but I can imagine it is also difficult for them. The nurses at CHEO have been amazing. Yes, I have had some very bizarre, inappropriate comments made to me in some cases, but all in all, we are very pleased with the care that Meredith is receiving. I didn't intend to condemn anyone. It dawned on me today why I hate to meet with the doctors so much—they are usually the bearers of bad news. When someone casually tells you that your baby's gag reflex is weak, you want to scream and say, "But did you see her perfect little pixie ears? What about her nose? And look at that incredible head of hair! Did you happen to feel her warm, perfect body against your skin or feel her heart beating? And those feet, and those toes…!" It is the negativity and the clinical examining of your precious and most beautiful creation that feels so wrong. That is what upsets me. Understanding the underlying cause of my anger and discomfort when meeting with doctors makes it all a little easier to deal with now. They are hoping to get her in for surgery within a week.

We have been lucky to get into the Cuddle Corner every day this week. Tomorrow is Tim's last full day with us until next weekend, as he starts back to work on Monday morning. We are not looking forward to adjusting to yet another change but we know we will manage. I plan to go to the hospital at noon and Tim will arrive after work around 4:30 p.m. We will eat supper there and leave for home around 6:30 p.m. This way, Meredith still gets one of us for six hours and Tim gets to see her each day. Tim and I also are able to eat dinner together and spend time with Meredith together. This is the plan for now. We'll see how it works. We also discovered today that if Meredith's surgery isn't scheduled until a couple of weeks from today that she may be moved to another floor. They need the beds for the babies who absolutely must be in intensive care. Meredith isn't sick enough right now to be there.

Sunday, January 4, 2004
We had a wonderful day today even though we couldn't get into a private room. Meredith is presently sharing her room with three other babies, all of whom are premature. Two seem fairly critical and the other is also quite serious. All three are very quiet. Sundays are generally calm in the unit. Rounds take less time and there is usually only one doctor and one nurse that make rounds, as opposed to the sometimes six doctors that make rounds on Monday morning.

Sadly, this was Tim's last full day with Meredith until next weekend, as he returns to work tomorrow after having had almost five weeks off. Thank goodness for that time off with everything we've been through. I can't imagine what it would have been like going through the last few weeks without Tim right beside me. We have had quite the adventure for lack of a better word! After Meredith was born, our midwife told us that things like this either bring a couple closer together or tear them apart. So far, this experience has brought us closer than we ever imagined. How could it not? It is such an amazing thing to create a new life especially when you have looked forward to it for so long. Then, when you're good and ready, voila, you find out that there is a life growing within you. And from that second onward, Tim and I were overjoyed and so very excited to meet our child.

Meredith now weighs 8 lb. 13 oz. She is growing well. Tomorrow we will find out when the surgery has been booked. We also found out that her hearing was tested, and as the nurse was explaining the test I was preparing myself to hear that Meredith is hearing impaired or deaf. At this point it has all been negative news so I wasn't too hopeful. Then I heard the words, "She passed the test!" I wanted to celebrate. We know now that she can hear and I am pretty sure she can see. These are the blessings that we would normally just take for granted. For us, it was great news.

Monday, January 5, 2004

Well, we made it through today…a day we weren't looking forward to. It turns out that it was kind of comforting to do something "normal." Tim got up for work and kissed me good-bye like he always does. Then I got up, and showered, and came downstairs, and things seemed "normal" for a change. My friend, Debi, arrived last night. We had asked her to come to give Meredith and us a Reiki treatment. It was nice to have the company on my first day at CHEO without Tim. When we arrived, our nurse came over and said she had heard we were unable to book the Cuddle Corner yesterday, so she took it upon herself this morning to reserve it for us today. I am eternally grateful to her. The day unfolded as usual. Meredith was fussy for a bit and then she slept in my arms for the rest of the day.

I arrived home at 4 p.m. and got dinner ready before Tim arrived at 5:30 p.m. His day went well too, although he missed Meredith and me terribly. We missed him too!!! Tomorrow, I will go in at noon and Tim will come to CHEO after work. We'll have supper there before heading home after rush hour traffic thins out. This arrangement should work very well for the three of us until Meredith comes home. We haven't heard when the surgery will be but hopefully we will know tomorrow.

Thursday, January 8, 2004

Since Tim has returned to work, the days have been long and we don't get home until 7:30 p.m. The NICU has been an absolute zoo and today we were asked to leave the Cuddle Corner as there was a family in distress that needed some private space. If I ever have a million dollars I will build more parenting rooms for the NICU. So today was spent in the regular room among the noise, beeps, alarms, chatter and all of the busyness of a NICU. The racket bothers me far more than it bothers Meredith. She startles at the loud noises but can sleep through almost everything. I may have to get a recording of the NICU to play for her when she gets home when we so she can sleep with familiar sounds.

This afternoon Tim and I met with one of two surgeons who will operate on Meredith. We feel confident handing our precious child to him. The date has been set for January 20. After about three to four days of recovery we should be able to bring her home. There will be a huge adjustment period, but eventually we will get back to living and enjoying our girl at home. I am sure the peace and calm of our home will be healing in itself. We must learn first how to feed her with the G-tube but I know that it will become second nature eventually. I am a little apprehensive about caring for Meredith. Everything seems so foreign, but I know that with time and patience, and a lot of help from friends and family, we will get used to each other and to everything new.

Meredith had the nasogastric tube (NG tube) that passes through her nose taken out the other night and replaced with a nasojejunal tube (NJ tube) that passes through the nose into the small bowel. The NJ tube has a weight at the bottom and migrates into the small intestine. This will hopefully relieve the reflux and vomiting so that she can get enough nutrients and strength before the surgery. It seems to be doing the trick. She has been less fussy and hasn't really been sick like before. We got a few photos of her without the tube in her nose, which was a treat. The new tube is fatter, and white, and stands out like a sore thumb. Soon the nose tube will be a thing of the past and we will be able to see her pretty face unobscured.

This experience is starting to wear us down, but we know the end is near, at least the end of this particular segment.

Friday, January 9, 2004

We made it through the first week with Tim at work and me spending time at CHEO solo. It went rather quickly actually, which was unexpected. I suspect Tim found it a little longer than I did. I am busy in the morning before heading out, and then the afternoon goes by fairly fast before Tim arrives at about 4:30 p.m. We have dinner and he holds Meredith. The two hours fly by and before long, it is time to settle her and head back home.

Today the Cuddle Corner was like Grand Central Station. A couple I doula-ed for two years ago just had their second baby. Unfortunately she had to come to CHEO immediately following her birth Tuesday morning. It has been kind of nice seeing familiar faces in the hallway. This morning I arrived to find our babies side-by-side in the same room. Who would have thought? Our doula, Tammy, drove the two hours from Wilno to see us, and even brought some food with her. Then, my friend (and doula), Susan, popped in unexpectedly to bring me a hands-free pumping kit, a gift from a lactation consultant and fellow doula here in Ottawa.

Saturday, January 10, 2004

Tim and I slept in a little this morning, and then went out for breakfast on our way to CHEO. My milk supply was a little low and I realize that I still need to eat for two! I was a little off this week being alone at CHEO with Meredith. I didn't have a lot of time and was not organized with snacks. That's changing though, as we just got home from a big grocery shop. We also picked up a portable stereo so that we can play music for her on our days in the Cuddle Corner.

We arrived to find Meredith sound asleep in her bed. We moved to the Cuddle Corner and before long, Tim had her out of bed and in his arms. We spent a wonderful day together. She awoke at 12:30 p.m. and was alert and bright all day. What a treat! She is starting to have many "awake" periods. She seemed to like the lullaby music we brought with us too.

We enjoyed spending a long day together as a family. Although this past week went by quickly, I really missed having Tim there with us. Only two more weeks of this, we hope, and then we can be home. We are anxious to bring Meredith home and begin the process of healing. We look forward to starting over and picking up where we left off. I imagine spending a whole day just lying in bed in the room where she was born and getting to know one another in our own space. After a while, I started feeling like I was co-parenting with all the nurses and staff at the hospital. It will be strange to bring her home and not have to answer to anyone. We can't wait to take her out to friends and family, and show her off. It will be such a joy to show her the outside world, the sunshine (when it warms up around here!), our home and all of the parts of our life that she has yet to encounter. We look forward to the day when she is at home with us longer than she was at CHEO.

Sunday, January 11, 2004

It took us an hour and 45 minutes to get into Ottawa this morning due to a snowstorm. We didn't realize how bad it was until we got on the road. We took our time and got to CHEO by 11 a.m.

Meredith was a fusspot last night apparently. Her nurse told us that she wouldn't stay in her bed. I had visions of Meredith climbing out of her crib and making a run for it! The nurse held her for two hours, and as soon as she put her down, Meredith awoke and was unhappy. Finally she put her in the swing and Meredith drifted off into sleepy land. **Note to self: get a swing!**

186

One of Meredith's roommates since day one was able to go home today. He had been at CHEO just over five months. How wonderful for his parents and for him. I couldn't imagine going in there for yet another 12 weeks, but I suppose if we had to we would. By the time we get Meredith home, she will be five days short of her two-month birthday. Who would have thought that we would be at CHEO for this long? Who would have thought we would end up at CHEO at all?

We arrived home to find our driveway shoveled anonymously by one of our neighbours—a random act of kindness. Tomorrow, we begin the last of two weeks (hopefully) at CHEO. Our future will involve appointments at CHEO most likely, but at least Meredith won't have to live there any longer.

Tuesday, January 13, 2004

I couldn't let another day go by without writing a quick update. I was with Meredith on my own yesterday and we had a fairly quiet day. We were moved to a different room and therefore separated from my client's baby who has been Meredith's "neighbour." Meredith is now sharing a room with three premature babies.

One of the hardest things to deal with is the thought of your baby being uncomfortable or upset and not tended to immediately. Having to trust the nurses who care for your baby is exceptionally difficult. I think a lot of these feelings are primal and difficult to explain. I know that many mothers out there would completely understand. One of my clients who is having her own CHEO experience has spoken about how tough she finds it. I can assure her that her feelings are very normal and that I, too, felt (and feel) the same things. It is unnatural to be separated from your baby immediately following birth, and then to have to leave them in a hospital each day. This can become unbearable. We are getting to that point now. We don't want to be apart from her anymore. We daydream about having her home and getting back to "normal." Spending a weekend at home and taking her out to show her off is something we look forward to.

The unit was hectic this morning, but soon we were able to get into the Cuddle Corner and settle in for some quiet time. Meredith had some reflux, but later cozied in to her Papa Keon's arms drifting into a deep sleep. She seems to enjoy the music we play for her now. This was Tim's second day without seeing Meredith, so I made some mini films and took photos for him. He will be counting the minutes until he can hold her tomorrow afternoon after work.

Thursday, January 15, 2003

We are arriving home later in the evenings and are exhausted these days. The mental stress is catching up. We are sleeping well but don't feel well rested. My sister-in-law said it was as if we had had a baby and then started a full-time job the following day. I know that all new parents are tired but this exhaustion is different somehow. It's the daily toll of getting organized every morning with baby laundry, packing snacks, bottles of milk, etc., and then driving an hour and an half into Ottawa, finding parking, and spending the day in a busy intensive care unit. I look at it as an adventure of sorts and know that "this too shall pass."

Tim was so happy to finally see Meredith Wednesday afternoon. He hadn't seen her since Sunday afternoon and was missing her. Just as we were getting ready to pack up, she awoke and was very upset, obviously in pain from reflux. We managed to help relieve her a bit. Awake and content, we had to leave her lying in her crib, looking around and listening to "Mozart for Mothers." We didn't get home until after 9 p.m.

I managed to get the large parenting room today, a real treat. Meredith and I got set up and I held her all day, as usual. She was awake and alert for most of the afternoon. We chatted and gazed at each other. Our midwife stopped in to say hello. She couldn't believe the changes in Meredith in just over a week. She is even starting to lose some of that great hair. I knew the day would come but I am sad to see it go nonetheless.

Tim arrived just in time to meet with a nurse who specializes in G-tube feedings. She sat with us for over an hour discussing the surgery and showing us a G-tube and how to care for it and feed with it. The tube itself was much larger than we had expected, but it will only be in for two to three months before she has a little button in its place. The nurse will train us along with the NICU nurses. They will not send us home until they (and we) are confident that we can handle it. Once at home we will have home care as well as support from this nurse. We will also have access to a dietitian to help us monitor Meredith, and increase her intake as required. The support we will have through all of this is phenomenal.

Thankfully there will be a lot of guidance as we take this unique journey into parenthood. It remains overwhelming and frightening at times, but we trust that everything is gradual, and that we will eventually learn to come to terms with it all. The fear of what might come is probably greater than the actual reality.

Not giving into fear and trusting that all that is handed to us will be manageable is the only way we can cope with something of this magnitude. I have moments where I think, "This is really happening. How could this be happening?" and then I take a breath and believe that this is how it is meant to be. There are no mistakes in life. There is a purpose to everything.

Friday evening, January 16, 2004

Meredith is six weeks old today and ever-changing. It is hard to believe that she will be two months old by the time we bring her home. We are sooooooo excited for this day. We know it will be an adjustment, but the joy of having her home, and finally living together will overshadow any challenges of this transition.

Mom and Dad picked me up this morning and spent the day with us at CHEO. We got the private parenting room again today and so we had a lot of space to move around in. Mom held Meredith all morning and into the afternoon. She couldn't believe how bright her eyes were. She sure gets a lot of compliments on those big, blue eyes of hers. Meredith slept then awoke around 2 p.m. fussing and fidgeting with reflux. Mom and Dad had to leave at 2:30 p.m. so I held Meredith for the next two hours until Tim arrived. Within minutes of his arrival she was sound asleep in his arms. Go figure! The time flew by as it always does and we were soon wheeling her back to her room. She was wide-awake when we left, but our nurse Heather promised that she would rock her if she didn't settle down.

Many mothers have commented that they don't know how I manage to leave my baby at CHEO, go home and sleep at night. Honestly if I thought too much about it after I left there I wouldn't have survived these last six weeks. If someone had told me that I would spend my first six weeks postpartum expressing milk every three hours, 24 hours a day, travelling the three hours each day to and from the hospital, witnessing the many procedures necessary for Meredith's health, I would have said there was no way I could ever handle it. But you know what? We don't get a choice in this.

You would be amazed at the strength you have within to get through these things. I have my moments where I don't think I can go on, or I don't think I will ever be able to handle what the future brings, but I know that I will because I have to. We are parents now and we are responsible for Meredith. We won't do her any good if we fall apart and throw in the towel. She needs us and we need her. When we get her home, we will first make up for the many nights spent apart from each another. We will never regain those first eight weeks; they are gone, but we have today and hopefully many tomorrows to make up for lost time.

Saturday, January 17, 2004

We were told that Meredith had a good night and that she is now a whopping 9 lb. 3 oz. We luckily got the Cuddle Corner for the day and booked the large parenting room for tomorrow, as we will have my sister Stephanie and her fiancé Robin with us.

Meredith slept in Tim's arms until about 3 p.m. when she awoke with a yelp. Again, we were dealing with an unhappy and uncomfortable baby. It is so painful to watch your child in pain. It brings me to tears to see her frowning and crying. We feel so helpless and she looks at us as if to say, "Can't you do anything?"

We had a visit from our neurologist today. I bolted as soon as he arrived as I cannot bear to hear anymore about Meredith's "condition." Tim had questions for him so he was happy to host him in the Cuddle Corner. I went next door and visited with my former clients and their baby. The good news is that Meredith is no longer showing signs of seizure activity. He was pleased to see her alertness and believes that she was following his face with her eyes, which means she can most likely see. The bad news is that Meredith is showing the classic signs of cerebral palsy, which Tim and I had expected. And so, we now begin the journey of learning more about this condition, and making plans for how we will help Meredith reach her full potential. Thankfully, the Ottawa Children's Treatment Centre (OCTC) will be with us to provide guidance and support over the next 18 years. In the midst of our joy and love for Meredith, we also must grieve the things that will never be. This is still a "wait and see" situation as they really cannot determine how severe things will become.

Sunday, January 18, 2004

It was an emotional day for us, as the reality of what we will deal with is beginning to hit us. We know that a part of this journey will be grieving, and that in order to get to a place of acceptance we must experience the sadness, anger, and grief. It is so frustrating to have to go through something so difficult. It's like you just want to stop everything for a moment to catch your breath, but this is a luxury you no longer have. You can only ride each day and each moment like a wave trusting that as the difficult feelings surface, so will the easier ones.

Tomorrow, I will spend the day alone with Meredith, and then on Tuesday, Tim and I will both be at the hospital first thing in the morning for Meredith's surgery. We pray that her surgeons have steady hands, and that Meredith heals quickly and smoothly from this operation. Her surgery is scheduled for 9:15 a.m. and will be about three and a half hours long. We are getting closer to bringing her home.

Monday, January 19, 2004

We just spoke with the surgeon. Meredith's surgery has been rescheduled for an hour earlier. We must be at CHEO by 7:30 a.m. to sign the consent form for surgery. I feel somewhat excited and relieved that the day has arrived. Meredith was so uncomfortable today and we cannot bear to see her furrowed brow and that frightened look on her face when she is in pain. It literally causes us pain. She will have a lot of healing after the operation not only healing the surgery site, but also the healing of her throat and esophagus from the chronic inflammation and ulcerations she has had to deal with from the NG tube. We can't wait for the next weeks to fly by until complete healing is accomplished. We are anxious to bring Meredith home to our "love nest" and to surround her with gentleness, peace, calm, love and laughter.

Tuesday, January 20, 2004

Meredith's surgery was a success and we are now at the beginning of the end of our stay at CHEO. We awoke at 5:15 a.m. to prepare for our 6:15 a.m. departure to CHEO. Tim was up even earlier, unable to sleep. I couldn't blame him. When we arrived at the NICU, we found Meredith on a warmer bed, ready for her operation. Beside her was a premature baby also being prepared for surgery this morning. He was having surgery on his heart. It was disturbing to see an IV in Meredith's head. They were unable to find a good vein in her hands or feet so a little bit of hair was shaved and an IV was placed in her head. It was difficult to see her like this. She was naked except for her diaper and was sleeping peacefully unaware of what was about to happen. Of course she awoke right before they came to get her, and so we had to watch her being wheeled into the operating room with those big, blue, innocent eyes staring back at us. We booked the parenting room so that we would have a private space to wait out the next three and a half hours.

We were expecting to see Meredith around 11:30 a.m. but time ticked away. Soon our family and friends, who had been there to support us, were on their way back to work and still there was no sign of Meredith. Finally the surgeon arrived at 1 p.m. to tell us that Meredith was in recovery and that all went well. They started later than they had anticipated. They were able to do laparoscopic surgery as opposed to opening her up. Thank goodness for small blessings!

We returned to her room to find our babe looking very rough. It was actually highly disturbing as we were thrown back in time to that first day we saw her after her birth. She had a respirator down her throat, the NG tube still in her nose, IVs in both of her hands, as well as the one in her head, the G-tube as well as tape on her belly over the little incisions that were cut for the surgery. She was quite pale too. We were told that she would come out of the anesthetic within a few hours, as they had to give her quite a large dose. Within about 15 minutes, she opened one eye and peeked at me, and then the other and then started waving her arm. The doctors were amazed that she was already coming out of the anesthetic. Thankfully, after her breathing stabilized, they took the respirator tube out of her throat, and soon she let out a very hoarse cry. Our poor little dove…

We were there to calm her and comfort her, as she tried to make sense of it all. Our nurse, Danielle, took the NG tube out, as well as one of the IVs from her hand. What a beautiful sight to see her sweet face free from tubes! Meredith was uncomfortable, so we asked the nurse to give her whatever drugs might make her more comfortable. She was sleeping soundly after Tim calmed her down, talking with her and stroking her head.

Meredith is a little fighter and we know that her spirit, her strength, her courage, and the love that surrounds her will help her through her future challenges. I look forward to writing about brighter days ahead as we get closer to bringing Meredith home.

Tomorrow we are touring the east wing on the fourth floor in preparation for Meredith's move there. Leaving the intensive care unit is another giant step of this journey to be home.

Thursday, January 22, 2004

Yesterday was one of the worst days so far. But it passed like others have, and today was better. One thing I know for sure: the bad days come but they always run their course making space for more joyful ones. And just when I start doubting that I'll be able to carry on, something happens to give me a boost, or I simply cry, and stomp my feet, and vent, and voila, I can see clearly once again. Yesterday was one of those days. I compared it to how women focus so much on their labours and births and then postpartum arrives and it hits them like a truck. Tim and I were so focused on this surgery that we didn't look past it. We were also under the impression that it was a relatively simple procedure, and that complications were not expected.

So when our baby was writhing in pain, and there was some miscommunication with pain medication, I reacted. Finally reaching the breaking point, I found myself freaking out. Our nurse, Danielle, who I consider an angel here on earth, saved the day when she was permitted to give Meredith a bolus of morphine.

There were many other horrendous and unexpected things that happened. Meredith was bleeding from the G-tube. Our nurse had never seen this before in 20 years of nursing. Our surgeon was rather perplexed about the whole thing as well. She ended up needing a blood transfusion. They had to re-insert the NG tube, as they needed to irrigate her stomach. It was a traumatic experience for Meredith. Tim and I came home feeling drained, beaten down, and completely frustrated with the situation. At some point, you want to ask, how could this possibly happen to an innocent child.

Today, however, things were different. Meredith's pain was under control and she was comfortable all evening and night. We had our "angel" nurse again today. Meredith's colour was better and she seemed to be much calmer. Tim took today off so that he could be present should anything go wrong, and just to be with Meredith. The last place he wanted to be was at work. He was just too distracted to focus on anything but Meredith. Now that she is stable, we are too. The bleeding from the tube has virtually stopped. Meredith settled in after that. We left her today feeling calm.

Tomorrow, she'll have an x-ray and tests to make sure the tube is in place, and that everything is healing as expected. She will resume her feedings of breast milk by the evening, hopefully, if everything is okay with the G-tube. Tonight, we will have a toast to a good day and will rest well in preparation for tomorrow's adventures at CHEO.

Friday, January 23, 2004

Meredith is seven weeks old today. This afternoon she said good-bye to the nurses in the NICU and moved to the fourth floor. She is sharing a room with three other babies who are monitored by two nurses. It is a change from the bustle of the NICU and we are grateful for this small step towards freedom. She started feeding through her G-tube at 6 p.m. tonight. She hadn't eaten since Monday night.

I went in around noon today with Mom and Dad and found Meredith lying awake in her crib facing the wall. When I started talking to her she turned her head towards my voice and looked up at me with her big, blue eyes. Mom held her for a long time while I expressed and ate lunch. Meredith seemed troubled earlier in the day. Every time a sudden noise was made she would jump and startle, and then cry. Finally she dozed off just in time to be awakened for a final check-up by the doctor. We moved up to the fourth floor around 3 p.m. accompanied by our nurse, Danielle. I wished she could have come with us.

Tim arrived at 4:30 p.m. and found Meredith snoozing in my arms. It was so good for us to see her comfortable. We had not seen her so content for such a long period of time. I know that she is healing and experiencing far less pain. She is not arching her back any more, or fussing like she did before the surgery. Now we'll focus on her feedings and hope that she tolerates them well. They're starting her off slowly and will gradually get her on to bolus feedings, presuming she is able to take in larger amounts of food. In the meantime, Tim and I will learn to feed her through the G-tube so that we are prepared to bring her home.

We accomplished a lot today. I am amazed at the strength of Meredith's soul. She manages to get through each day working hard to be healthy. She has no concept of time. I wonder if she thinks to herself, "So, this is life? This sucks!" I want her to get better and strong as soon as possible. We can't wait to show her off to the world. Her aunt knitted her a pair of "party socks" for her homecoming party, which we will have one day.

Sunday, January 25, 2004

Meredith had another good day, although she was a little fussier this afternoon. We vented her G-tube three times and this made all of the difference. We are getting the hang of things. I suppose it's like this with any baby, learn-

194

ing what the problem might be when your baby cries or fusses, and then attempting to find the solution. In our case, venting takes the place of burping.

Meredith did an amazing thing this morning. She sucked on her fist for the first time! We had tried to get her to do this weeks ago but stopped when she refused to soothe herself this way. Today, however, she was doing it on her own without any coaching. We were told that she had grabbed the nurse's finger and tried to suck on it earlier in the morning, and so the nurse offered a soother to her. Meredith sucked on it for a bit but lost interest. It is a start and a huge jump from what we have been seeing the past six weeks. We gave her a sponge bath today. She wasn't too pleased as she prefers to be bathed in a tub. She was sparkling by the time we were through and smelled delicious. Tim held her for most of the day to make up for the short time he has with her on the weekdays.

We are enjoying the fourth floor. The nurses are great and the room we are in has a more positive feel. There are two babies here from Baffin Island and another baby from Ottawa. Three of the four babies have just had G-tube surgery in the past week. Meredith and one other boy had a fundoplication as well. There are huge windows in these rooms, and today with the curtains wide open, the sun shone through. Meredith had never felt the sun on her face before. The doctors came in for rounds this morning and were upbeat and positive. It's a completely different environment, understandably. The NICU deals with babies who are in critical condition. We are happy to have moved up in the world. Once we leave CHEO and time passes, we will look back at our time here and remember only the positive things. The negative will pale in comparison.

I am so grateful to CHEO. The care they provided saved Meredith's life. She wouldn't be with us had it not been for the extraordinary team that arrived at our community hospital on the night of her birth, and the nurses and doctors who watched over her for the past seven weeks. With that said, we would be happy never to set foot in CHEO again!

So, we pray for healing and an uncomplicated recovery for Meredith. We pray for the strength to keep up with our daily CHEO visits. We pray that Meredith will continue to dazzle us with her little achievements.

Tuesday, January 27, 2004

We had a horrible day yesterday. Just when we think that the day has come that will break us down, it passes, and the following day is the complete opposite. It really is amazing how dreadful one day can be compared to the next.

I walked into Meredith's room yesterday to find her in the arms of Jean, a hospital volunteer who comes in on Mondays to hold babies. I was told by one of the nurses that Meredith was possibly fighting an infection. What next? The doctor informed me as soon as I arrived that they would have to do an in and out catheter on Meredith to get a urine sample. All I could think was, "How much more can we take?" Just when we think we can breathe a sigh of relief, we're hit with something else. You get to a point where you want to just laugh at the ridiculousness of it all.

The young doctor informed me that catheters weren't invasive. I asked if he had ever had a catheter, and he said that he had not. I pointed out that catheters were indeed invasive and quite painful. Soon the surgeon arrived and checked out her G-tube, the dressings were changed, and then it was time for the catheter. After holding her wee face in my hands, while she screamed bloody murder, it was over and I held her in my arms for the rest of the afternoon. After Tim arrived and took over on the cuddling duties, Meredith suddenly exploded in a rage, and our nurse found that she had blown a vein in her foot at the site of the IV. As soon as it was removed, Meredith relaxed. Watching her screaming in pain, AGAIN, was just more then we could bear. We arrived home weary and feeling extremely sad and frustrated. And then night came and we slept and awoke to yet another day.

I arrived to the hospital eager to improve upon yesterday. Meredith was snoozing when my dad and I walked into the room. She had to have some blood work done first thing, so I held her hands while she was poked, and then Dad held her while I expressed milk and ate. Meredith was happy and calm all day. I gave her a bath and washed her hair. The rest of the babies in our room were also content so it was a fairly peaceful day. We had many visitors drop by which was nice. Dad left around 2 p.m. Meredith and I just sat and cuddled until Tim came after work. Meredith had her dressings changed again so we bravely sat through that trying to comfort her. This procedure doesn't really hurt her but she is very sensitive to procedures being done to her. We cannot blame her.

We are learning about feedings. It's certainly not rocket science. Tim and

I are confident that we'll have it mastered in no time at all. Meredith is up to her full feedings, and so now we just have to work on getting to bolus feeds providing her with a good amount of food at one time, as opposed to continuous feeds. We are grateful for the strength that gets us through the really rough days, and grateful for the days that are gentle on our babe, and on our souls.

Wednesday, January 28, 2004

Meredith and I spent most of the day attached although a volunteer came by around 3 p.m. and held her for me so that I could express. Meredith was awake and alert throughout the day. She tends to mix up nights and days so we usually spend a very sleepy day together. Today was different. She was also somewhat fussy, but it was kind of entertaining as she makes these squeaky sounds like she is talking to us, or maybe complaining to us about what she has been through.

Tim arrives at the usual 4:30 p.m. time and we close our day snuggling and chatting with Meredith. We had a couple of visitors today, which was nice. Meredith is meeting more people all the time. I was able to take a walk in the halls after I detached Meredith from the IV pole. That was the first time we could move from her crib unhindered. It was exciting to stroll the halls without fear of pulling something out, or having to drag a pole along. I showed her the outside world through a window, though she didn't seem too interested. One day we'll take her on a tour in her stroller that awaits her at home.

Thursday, January 29, 2004

What a busy little bee Meredith was today. She was awake for much of the day, and mostly by choice, although she did have some visits from various caregivers. The physiotherapist met her and showed us some simple exercises we can start to encourage Meredith to move her muscles in the opposite way that she tends to move them. We are to encourage her to turn her head to the left more by holding her in our right arms only, placing a folded receiving blanket under her head when she sleeps. She will need to examine Meredith's right shoulder blade further to see what exercises we can do for her neck. We are also gently uncurling her thumb, encouraging it to open and relax in this position. We are flexing her wrists as they have a tendency to curl inwards. We are eager to get started on these exercises that will help Meredith over time.

197

The physiotherapist plans to stop in tomorrow to teach us more exercises. Meredith seemed to enjoy all of the stretching and moving and didn't squawk at all.

Tim was late getting in tonight, as there were problems at work just as he was leaving. When he arrived, I passed Meredith to him, and they had their cuddle time. She slept peacefully and awoke a few times. I spoke to Tim about our busy day and showed him some new exercises. It is unfortunate that when major events happen in your life that the whole world doesn't stop moving for a moment. Practical chores like paying bills, work, and household tasks seem so unimportant in comparison. I know that if Tim could, he would spend every minute of his day with Meredith. Unfortunately, bills need to be paid and in order for that to happen someone has to work.

We will stimulate Meredith, and do everything and anything suggested that might help her progress, and help her to reach her full potential. This weekend Tim will do all feedings, as he hasn't had much opportunity to practice. I am getting pretty good at it now. I do the odd silly thing like forgetting to clamp the tube, resulting in spilling milk everywhere after detaching from Meredith. You do these things once or twice, and then you won't do it again. I find I learn better by doing, so I just laugh and carry on.

This is by far the most difficult experience of our lives. It is a day-by-day thing. If we start finding ourselves thinking too far into the future, we quickly become overwhelmed, and panicked about what might be. The key word here is "might", as this is such a "wait and see" kind of condition. Cerebral palsy has so many different levels, and so many faces, that we will not know all of Meredith's ins and outs until time passes. This is probably the toughest part because we cannot fully accept anything, because we don't know what we're dealing with and having to accept. Our imaginations are our greatest enemy in all of this. We are slowly (Tim more than me) beginning to do research on cerebral palsy and gathering information. It is a hard pill to swallow. There are good days and bad and such an array of emotions involved. We have found that the only way to cope is to feel ALL of the feelings that come up, to talk about them, and to vent, to somehow manage to find humour in our days, to laugh, to give each other a lot of love and affection, and to keep up the practical things like eating well, drinking lots of water, and getting good amounts of sleep. Above everything, we love our little Meredith, our greatest accomplishment and most beautiful creation.

The pediatrician spoke with us today about Meredith's feedings. Tomorrow we will begin the process of getting Meredith on to bolus feedings. The goal is to feed her every three hours. Each feeding will take an hour. Presently she is on continuous feeds. He expects, if all goes well, that we will be able to bring her home two weeks from tomorrow. We won't count on it, but are hopeful.

Thursday, February 5, 2004

So much has happened over the past few days. We have been visited steadily by so many professionals that I can hardly keep track of who's who, and of what acronym means what. We have met with occupational therapists, physiotherapists, doctors from the Ottawa Children's Treatment Centre (OCTC), the homecare case manager, the G-tube nurse specialist, and the list goes on. It is a little overwhelming at times but I know that things will settle down once we are home. My sister, Lana, dropped in last night for a visit after work, and was shocked at the noise and the stress level of the room we are in. I find it so much less hectic than the NICU. I can just imagine how amazing it will be to be home for good, to enjoy peace and quiet.

The best news this week is that Tim and I are picking Meredith up Saturday morning for a weekend pass! We will return her to the care of CHEO on Monday morning. There are still the last bits of discharge paperwork to be done, and so she must remain there a few more days past the weekend. The end is very near, and if things continue as they are, we expect to have her home for good by the end of next week. Tim and I have both mastered the feedings, and I have done the dressing changes a few times. By April, Meredith should have her little button in place instead of the tube so the dressings will be no longer be an issue. Her portable pump is expected to arrive within eight weeks of having her home. In the meantime, we should have a collapsible IV pole so we are able to leave the house occasionally. Once that portable pump arrives...look out!—we'll be on the road touring in no time. Meredith is doing well. She gets very upset at times, but only when there is a good reason, otherwise she is calm and content, looking around, or is asleep. She loves her new mobile that our friend, Jody, brought to the hospital for her. She is mesmerized by it, and loves the classical music that it plays.

I've been thinking a lot lately about happiness and how different people have different reactions to their circumstances. Perceptions and choices seem to determine whether we are happy or not. Cynicism, bitterness, and anger are choices. It is important to experience a range of emotions from our tougher experiences of life, but it is equally crucial to let them wash over you. If one does not allow them to surface, to truly express them, then we get stuck there and cannot move forward. I have had days when I was seriously angry at how unfair (or what I have perceived as unfair) this situation is. This anger is accompanied by fear, tremendous fear. I give myself the space and the permission to stomp my feet, vent, and wallow, because I know that this is the only way these feelings will soften and make space for joy, happiness, and peace. I don't intend to waste my life being miserable. Meredith deserves more than that.

Sunday, February 15, 2004

Days have flown by, and here we are in the middle of February. As I type with one hand, Meredith is lying in my arms in her own home, at least for the next two days! We had a great night of sleep except for one hour between 4 a.m. and 5 a.m. when she was quite fussy. She went back to sleep and then awoke in time to be held by her daddy. We have been trying in the last 48 hours since she's been home, to figure out a schedule that will work, so that Tim gets to care for Meredith as much as possible, and we both get enough rest to function. The feeding schedule looks easy on paper. She is fed for one hour every three hours. After the feeding begins, you can sleep, and then get up after the hour to vent and flush her tube and rinse out the feeding equipment. Then, there is a two-hour break before the next feed starts. However, if Meredith is uncomfortable, gassy, fussy, awake, or unsettled, sleep is out of the question. We are hoping to eventually get rid of the 3 a.m. feeding. So far, so good.

It's as though our first six to eight weeks of normal postpartum transition were put on hold. When we brought Meredith home last week we weren't expecting the emotional outpouring, exhaustion and general anxiety that accompanied it. We had put our time in over the past ten weeks and didn't think there would be an adjustment period. When we returned her to CHEO on Monday we knew we had to get ourselves organized with support for the next few weeks. I knew that we were going to experience the overwhelming shock of having a baby in our home, realizing that as her parents we must now raise her. I knew it would hit us like a freight train, a delayed reaction due to the realities of our first ten weeks with Meredith. All along we have had to shut down a part of ourselves in order to cope with the daily life of having a baby in the hospital. To maintain our sanity and leave her each night at the hospital, we had to shut off a part of our hearts and head. Suddenly, Meredith was in our living room, and we realized, "She is OUR baby." It was in that couple of days that I realized the depth of trauma that I personally experienced in the last ten weeks. These mini-traumas range from having first responders walk into our bedroom and scoop Meredith up within minutes of her birth, to witnessing her being poked, prodded, tested, and operated on, not to mention the weeks of watching her in pain from reflux.

And so, we decided to get organized and jump in with both feet and bring her home, even though the hospital offered to give us a few more weekend passes. Although we were headed into unknown territory and felt apprehensive, we also knew that delaying wouldn't make this journey easier. The CHEO journey was difficult and exhausting. We felt that the best place for Meredith to continue to grow was in our home where she belonged.

Our first night home was busy as expected. Meredith was a little out of sorts and awake for most of the night, although she wasn't cranky by any means. We managed to grab some small naps in the day yesterday, and then set up a room downstairs as a temporary nursery complete with a single bed for the caregiver. My mom arrives today for a week, and then we will call on our friends and family to come out during the days to allow me a nap here and there. We are also eligible for a relief worker to come into our home. I figured we would round up as much support as we could and that hopefully, in the end we would find that we didn't need the help at all, or for as long as anticipated. At least we know it is there, should the need arise.

This week, Meredith will meet her dietitian and the occupational therapist. We will also hear from the infant development worker and physiotherapist. We are visited by a registered nurse each day who checks Meredith's vital signs and answers any questions we might have regarding the feeding pump.

Good news this week! We learned that although it is common for babies who have suffered hypoxia to have damaged cochlea, thankfully, both cochlea in Meredith's ears are healthy, and sounds are making their way to her brain. In a year from now we will find out if her brain is organizing the sound. At least we know she has passed step two of three.

She had to have another EEG on Thursday, as she reacted strangely after she was given a vaccination, and they thought she might be having a seizure.

Her EEG was the same as the one she had back in her early days. It showed abnormalities but did not show seizure activity. This doesn't mean she won't develop seizures, but at least we know she is not experiencing seizures right now. Life is never boring around here.

Sunday, February 22, 2004

We have one week under our belt. We feel a little less overwhelmed however, the rough days come, and then thankfully leave. When they arrive you think you may never get through the day. Exhaustion brings with it fears and worries about the future. This also stirs up the ever-present grief that resides just below the surface. But we know now that the difficult times pass and we bask in the moments that bring joy.

Meredith struggled to adjust when she first arrived home. We started to think that they may have been sedating her in the hospital and hadn't informed us. We adjusted her feedings, as we felt she was being overfed on the schedule she was on. This seems to have helped. She is choking and gagging much less now. It has been tricky trying to figure out when she needs to be left alone as opposed to being held, but we're learning.

Professionals have marched through our house this week and there are more to come. We are doing occupational therapy exercises during feeds so that Meredith can connect feeling full with oral stimulation. I manage to get her physio completed after her bath when she is calm and relaxed.

We have a manageable schedule between my mom, Tim and me, but things will change now that Mom has left. My mom has been an amazing help to all of us. We had some deep conversations in the wee hours of the morning that I will remember and treasure forever. Our freezer has a week's worth of meals that Mom whipped up while she was here. She had a wonderful time getting to know Meredith. Having an experienced mother on board as I adjusted to my role as a full-time mother was wonderful.

Tim is off work this week so we will spend the next seven days getting to know Meredith and adjusting to our new baby girl. Sleep deprivation may become an issue. We'll assess this daily and then call in the troops when we feel that we're losing ground. I am still expressing milk too, which may become more difficult as time goes on. I always said that I would do it as long as I was able. So far it is the best thing I can give to Meredith, and it makes me feel good knowing that although the mode of delivery isn't optimal, at least she is getting breast milk.

All in all, it is good to be home and we trust that the days and weeks ahead will get easier with time and experience. We pray Meredith will benefit from the physio and occupational therapy, and that her body and mind will respond to the care and love that surrounds her.

Saturday, February 28, 2004
I am very pleased to announce that Tim and I FINALLY experienced what is known as a "babymoon." We have spent an incredible week together with Meredith adjusting, learning, laughing and loving. Besides the not-so-normal activities like tube feeding we have had a week that resembled what I had always imagined having our baby home would be like. While about three months behind, this feeling arrived, and for that we are grateful.

Mom left last Sunday afternoon. Tim and I jumped into our roles as full-time parents without nursing or family assistance. Meredith has been patient and tolerant as we fumble and get to know her unique ways. We realize that with or without cerebral palsy, Meredith is our baby girl, and she will be who she is. Everything will come gradually and we will deal with each issue as they arise.

I remember how horrified we were at Christmas time when the doctor mentioned the possibility of a G-tube. I remember thinking it couldn't be worse. I couldn't imagine feeding her through a tube in her stomach. The thought of having an IV pole in our home with a plethora of other medical supplies was a great cause of stress. Yet here we are, doing our thing and feeling it is so normal. We don't think twice about setting up her feedings, "plugging" her in, venting her when she is gassy, changing her dressings after her bath, and all these necessary tasks. In fact, we have had to remember that for visitors this method of feeding might make some people uneasy and uncomfortable. We're hoping that as friends and family see our comfort around it that they too will accept it as Meredith's "norm" and eventually it won't seem so strange.

It has been really good to have Tim home this week so he could have an opportunity to meet the professionals who will work with Meredith on a regular basis. Our occupational therapist, Carol, showed us some techniques to stimulate Meredith while she is feeding. We stroke the tip of her tongue, rub her gums, and massage her jaw. She, in turn, starts breathing quickly and salivates, getting very excited. Tim has even had some small successes with the soother. We are careful not to push her too hard. When she clamps down with her jaw, or shows signs of stress, we stop. We want to gain her trust and help her to associate pleasure with feeling her belly fill up with milk.

We had our first visit with the infant development worker. She brought a seat for Meredith to sit in, as well as some wedge pillows, and a mirror. There are some terrific programs in Lanark County that Meredith will be able to participate in as she grows. One that really grabbed our attention was the Therapeutic Riding Program. This involves horseback riding for anyone over the age of two who has developmental or physical disabilities. We were told that they have children as young as two, and stroke patients in their 70s who take part in the program. Sitting on the horse helps with core body strength and balance. There is also something with the horse's movement that helps with walking. There are five farms in Lanark County that have the specially trained horses.

There is also a Language Development Program, Family Relief Program, Summer Day Camps, and Residential Camps and many family activities throughout the year designed for children with special needs. We look forward to meeting other families who share similar challenges. A whole new world awaits us.

Meredith met her family doctor this week, a mere five-minute walk from our house. It was our big outing this week and it went very well. With the busy activity in the waiting room we were sure Meredith would be a wreck but she was fine. She is now 56.5 cm long and weighs 9 lb. 12 oz. She is a wee thing but we are pleased. She has gained 5 oz. since being home. We expect a continual gain, and eventually we hope to move out of the fifth percentile! I think that being home will make a huge difference in her growth. The doctor wasn't concerned, and we made an appointment to return in a month for her next set of vaccinations. We are welcome to pop by the office anytime to have her weighed. I will make it a weekly outing for a little while until I see that she is progressing well.

Yesterday, Meredith's Nanny and Poppa drove down from Cobden and babysat Meredith for an hour and a half so that Tim and I could go out on a date. We walked to a quaint little restaurant situated along the Mississippi River and had a wonderful lunch. We promised each other that our conversation would not revolve around Meredith! It was so nice to feel safe leaving her with family and to have time for a celebratory lunch in honour of our first week home together as a family.

Today we took Meredith out for her first walk in her stroller. The weather is supposed to be beautiful this week so I plan to get her out every day that I can. We wanted our first walk to be together as a family. The sunshine and fresh air was so good for her and for us. We planned only a short excursion, but Meredith did so well that we walked all the way to the grocery store, picked up some things and then walked home. We were surprised that the noisy traffic on Main Street didn't upset her, but she did start to fuss in the very last minutes of the walk.

Tim returns to work on Monday so another interesting week awaits us. My dad comes on Monday for a visit. My sister, Stephanie, is coming Tuesday and Wednesday and sister, Lana, will come Thursday and Friday to help out. We are feeling confident and capable though. We hope things will continue to get easier as we learn more everyday about Meredith. We know that there will be rough times too but that's life. We are confident that we will overcome those rough times with love, support and patience, and a little humour.

Sunday, March 7, 2004

Week three "postpartum" has brought us even further ahead. Slowly but surely, we are adjusting to family life. It is still strange sometimes when I think that Meredith is here with us. It was a year ago this weekend that Meredith was conceived. What miracles our children are!

It is 6 a.m. as I write and Meredith is finally settled and having her "breakfast." Unfortunately, she had a rough night. She has been hacking since her surgery and it has worsened over time. Originally they speculated her stomach retching was just getting accustomed to milk again. Then after a couple of weeks we were told that perhaps it was saliva remaining in the back of her throat due to her weak swallowing ability. The hospital air was dry and so she may not have had an issue there as a result. But now we are six weeks post-op and the retching has become fairly severe. I am wondering if something went wrong with the surgery. She shouldn't be able to bring anything up from her stomach. She isn't supposed to be able to burp and we've heard her do that. They never really did find out why she had complications after her surgery. It's all a little nerve wracking. During the night she awakes gagging. I leap out of bed to help her. Last night she gagged, hacked and was uncomfortable until 5:30 a.m. when she got some relief. She is now calm and resting.

Tomorrow we have our follow-up visit with the surgeon. He will check out Meredith's G-tube site, and measure her for her feeding tube, the flat button that will replace the feeding tube. It is more discreet and will eliminate the daily dressing changes. It will also be less irritating for Meredith's skin and provide more freedom since we won't be dealing with a long tube getting in the way. Our visit to CHEO will be the first trip where we will use the portable pump. We will be far from home when a feeding is due. This will provide a good opportunity to practice and give us another step towards freedom. We also hope to get some answers to some of our health questions.

Our week was busy. I don't know how I will manage when I am on my own. Thankfully, I have had someone here every day so far. My sister Lana will continue to visit every Thursday and Friday until she begins working full time. I hope that in a week or so I will have figured out how to organize so we can get everything done in the day. It looks fairly straightforward on paper, but between physiotherapy, occupational therapy, chair time, expressing, eating, feedings, baths and dressing changes, napping and dealing with the regular visits by professionals, it all seems overwhelming. All I can do is prioritize and keep things in perspective.

Many people have offered to visit us, and we are happy to have company along the way. We still feel like new, vulnerable, postpartum parents and need more time to grow in our confidence. With all that takes place here in a day, I know that I would feel stressed if I wanted to visit with someone and couldn't. I know that things will become more routine and that as Meredith grows, she will get into more of a groove. We hope to get out for many walks in the spring. The sun is shining today and we will go for a walk this afternoon. I suppose it's a good thing that I do not have much to write about. Could it be that we have reached the time of "when things settle down a little?"

Monday, March 15, 2004:   FINAL UPDATE, FOR THE TIME BEING
We have had a shift in the last week. It's amazing how things just click somehow. Everything seems easier and less daunting. Meredith has somewhat of a routine, but is rebellious like her mother and doesn't always comply. We are enjoying the visits by her "other" caregivers. They are all respectful, positive and knowledgeable. Today, our infant development worker stopped in on her own time to drop off a couple of books that she thought we might find helpful. I have already read one of them. I am not feeling as alone, and know

that the complexity of what I feel is "normal." It helps to have your feelings and thoughts validated. Meredith weighed in on Thursday at 10 lb. 2 oz. She gained six ounces in two weeks. Slowly but surely...

These past 14 weeks and three days (I've been counting!) have been the most difficult and yet the most incredible of our lives. The feelings of sadness constantly compete with feelings of utter joy. There have been good days and bad days, however, as time passes and the initial shock wears off, the good days greatly outnumber the tough ones. We are grateful and know that the support we have received from our community, colleagues, friends and especially our dear families, have brought us through the dark days that we thought would never end. The love and strength of those who surround us have carried us through.

I feel I have experienced every emotion and have had every personal thought and belief challenged by this experience. I have questioned my spiritual faith among other beliefs. I have asked such questions as, "What kind of a God would allow the suffering of babies?" and "Why did this happen to us?" and "What did we do to deserve to see our baby in pain?" In the end, these questions were simply a reaction to tremendous grief, shock and bewilderment. Tim and I have always known, even in the midst of the rawest emotions, that we are blessed in so many ways. If we could change anything, it would be to stop the pain and suffering that Meredith has had to go through. This has been, to this day, the hardest thing for us as parents.

We are finding that there is often so much emphasis placed on Meredith's medical issues that the little person that Meredith is and is becoming is overlooked. She is far more than this condition known as cerebral palsy.

Tuesday, March 23, 2004

We had our first weekend away this past weekend and it was wonderful! Our first mini holiday was, of course, a visit to both sets of grandparents in their homes. I heard that they were very excited in anticipation of our arrival. My dad said that he was giddy while shopping for groceries the afternoon of our arrival. Meredith travelled well and we had a good night away from home.

We have a big day at CHEO on Thursday, March 25. Meredith is having a milk study done, and then she gets her feeding tube in the afternoon. No more tube to deal with. Just a flat porthole of entry into her stomach. We rejoice over these very strange, but now normal things. We have come a long way!

Sunday, April 18, 2004

It has been confirmed that Meredith is experiencing infantile seizures. In the past few weeks we had witnessed her spasms and weren't concerned until they started becoming more intense, and lasting for longer periods of time. Their repetitiveness also raised concerns. At our neurology follow-up appointment at the end of March we described this behaviour to the doctor. He immediately recognized them as seizures and immediately ordered an EEG. The EEG came back negative for seizure activity, puzzling the neurologist. We saw him again this past Thursday and after another EEG, it showed positive and definite signs of seizures. Sadly, Meredith is now on anti-seizure medication. We are hoping that it works. The next option for medication causes irritability and sleeplessness. I'm not sure Tim and I could cope with that right now.

Babies can grow out of these seizures by the age of 18 months but many go on to develop childhood seizures. We are grateful to have caught them early and hope that they can be controlled by this medication. We are already seeing slight changes in the amount and intensity of the seizures. The seizures are very hard on Meredith and we wonder now if the retching problem is connected somehow.

We spoke with the surgeon last week and Meredith's mid-March milk study came back normal. The reflux is no longer an issue and the milk is emptying well from her stomach. With the seizures and retching, Meredith and I can't really go out in the car alone. It would be wonderful to manage these symptoms, and for Meredith and I to have some freedom to leave the house.

Meredith continues to receive physio, infant development and occupational therapy. Two weeks ago Tim tried the soother again. Lo and behold, Meredith took it and sucked on it a little. The next day the occupational therapist came by and was so pleased with how Meredith was able to use her tongue. We hadn't been doing a lot of oral stimulation with her, as Meredith was struggling to adjust to increased feedings. She would gag when we went near her mouth. The OT suggested we work with the soother at one feeding per day and if we got some sucking action at least twice a week that would be good progress. She is going to be thrilled when she sees Meredith on Tuesday. Meredith is now sucking like she has always used a soother. She has a great suck and when she pauses and you tug on the soother, she hangs on to it and starts sucking again. I was in tears watching her. She has made huge progress in a short time. We are feeling confident that drinking from a bottle, and maybe even attempts at the breast, are no longer impossible dreams.

Our other news is that we moved Meredith's crib upstairs and I have returned to sleeping in bed with Tim. For the past nine weeks, I have slept downstairs in a single bed by Meredith's crib. She is now in her own room across the hall. We bring everything upstairs at night so that we don't have to navigate downstairs. The first two nights have been successful and we feel we are making headway in reaching normalcy. Meredith is a great sleeper anyway and so we only have to get up for feedings and to change her diaper once during the night. She usually wakes up around 2 a.m. and then drifts back to sleep within 20 minutes or so. We are thankful for small blessings!

Meredith has graduated to bathing in the big tub as of today. Her baby tub is too small for her now. She seemed content in the tub today and didn't squawk at all. She weighs about 11 lb. 5 oz., but it could be a little more by now. I will have her weighed this week again. We get out for walks in the stroller when the weather is good.

We spent Easter weekend with family in Cobden and Bristol, Quebec. She met most of her extended family. It was our first holiday celebration with Meredith. She travelled well, except for our drive back on Easter Sunday when she cried from Bristol to Almonte, a one and a half hour journey! Regardless, we look forward to many more trips with her.

Sunday, May 16, 2004
It's hard to believe a month has passed since my last entry. There is never a dull moment around here. Most days, I wish we could be bored for a while. Just when we let our guard down something challenges our strength and stamina yet again.

We are back at CHEO and have been here since May 6. We gratefully got a weekend pass but will return tomorrow morning with hopes of getting some answers. Meredith started retching more violently. This coincided with new anti-seizure medication (the first didn't work out). We were told that the anti-seizure medication that she is on now produces extra secretions in the body, explaining the increased retching. The other concern is that theoretically, Meredith should not be able to bring anything up from her stomach since the fundoplication surgery in January.

We were put in isolation upon our arrival as Meredith was tested for everything just to be sure. She had developed a dry cough that seemed to trigger the retching but did not exhibit any other symptoms of illness. We are on

4-East where we spent four weeks on our last stint at CHEO. Meredith has a lot of friends here. People were coming in to visit and commented on how much she had grown. These comments were a welcome change, from general comments on how small she was for her age and asking if she was premature. It's hard to believe she was 8 lb. at birth and now weighs just 11 lb., 6 oz. She was starting to lose weight when this crazy retching began. It really concerned us as she cannot afford to lose any weight.

When things turned from bad to worse, I was away with Meredith visiting my parents. We had planned to be there for a week but our visit was cut short by all of this. By Thursday we were on our way home to pick up Tim, and then off to CHEO Emergency to be admitted.

I spent my first Mother's Day in CHEO. It wasn't a big deal to me though as I was simply grateful to have experienced pregnancy, childbirth and now, motherhood. Tim brought his laptop and had created a mini-movie from photographs of Meredith sleeping. There were quotations at the end about mothering, strength and facing your fears. It was so beautiful. I, of course, bawled when I saw some of the photos from our earliest days. We got take-out and ate in the hospital room. It was nice to have a private room for a few days. Then, at midnight, our nurse informed me that we were being moved to a shared room. Our roommates turned out to be amazing. We had a good time in the three days that we were together.

Being back at CHEO this time has been a different experience. We are feeling far more confident as parents. We have avoided many unnecessary rectal temperatures, as well as other routine procedures that only serve to aggravate Meredith. We didn't have our first test until Monday. Although it showed that Meredith didn't have reflux, she retched the barium within an hour. The big milk study test was on Friday and it showed that Meredith, again, is not refluxing. We find all of this perplexing. The surgeons believe the fundoplication is still intact and has not loosened or let go. This good news means that Meredith will not have to undergo another surgery. The bad news though is that we are still trying to figure out what is going on.

It is highly likely that this vicious cycle is brought on by the anti-seizure medication. Meredith may be producing more secretions triggering her coughing, which in turn triggers retching. Now that problems with the fundoplication have been ruled out, the next step will involve neurology. Meredith has also had blood work done to determine whether or not she has a milk protein allergy. It turns out that she doesn't. I would feel terrible knowing that my milk due to my dairy consumption was making her sick all of this time. Now we are waiting on results to find out if Meredith has a urinary tract infection.

I was feeling pretty unhinged after spending 24 hours a day at CHEO except for the two nights when at home. I have only been home one night since leaving for my parent's home two weeks ago. Tim and I were thrilled to sleep in our own bed Friday night and have Meredith in her own crib. Yesterday, we straightened the house, barbequed steak, roasted garlic and had a bottle of good, red wine. We rented a couple of movies and headed to bed early. This weekend has been relaxing and has rejuvenated us enough to face the week ahead.

This morning we met our family relief worker who will assist us with Meredith when we leave here for short periods of time for errands, appointments and dates. She's young and energetic and seems very suitable. We'll begin our training sessions once we're home from CHEO and settled.

Sunday, June 6, 2004

We arrived home on Friday, May 21 on another weekend pass. The deal was that if Meredith was fine by Monday then we could stay home, but if things weren't going well, there was a bed at CHEO to return to. Happily, everything seemed to be well, so we opted to stay home.

I'll just backtrack a little...We ended up returning to CHEO on the Monday after the last entry and had been moved into the room where we were back in January and February. We were also placed in the same bed so it was a bit of a déjà vu. One of the babies who was there last time was in again, so it began to feel like the last three months at home were a dream.

We went in feeling optimistic that things would be sorted out and then I was told that the neurologist on-call wanted to increase the Nitrazepam (the drug that was causing problems). He felt getting the seizures under control was the priority. Meredith had been having mild seizures since starting the Nitrazepam. I thought preventing her choking to death was more important so I refused his recommendation until I spoke with our neurologist who I have grown to trust. Within an hour of being paged our neurologist arrived to speak with me. After I explained what Tim and I thought the problem was he agreed, and made a decision to begin weaning Meredith off the Nitrazepam and trying Sabril again. This meant another few days at CHEO to be certain

211

Meredith would react well to the Sabril.

By Friday, May 21 we were home. Meredith had her first screaming fit accompanied by abdominal, intestinal cramping and gas. The episode lasted for an hour. Since then, the fits have gotten worse. She was having these episodes one or two times a day. I visited our family doctor on Wednesday, May 26, and he believed it was a reaction to the medications. Our neurologist does not believe the fits to be a side effect. Our family doctor suggested we continue as we are for a week and hope to see improvement as her body continues to adjust to the new drug and the old drug leaves her system.

It has been a week and a half since visiting the family doctor and it's been a very rough week. We experienced three sleepless nights followed by days when Meredith was unable to nap. Meredith's discomfort has increased in frequency. We are frustrated and sleep deprived. We are unsure how long we can cope. She has had a good couple of days, and last night was better so perhaps things are starting to improve? When we left the hospital two weeks ago, Meredith weighed 11 lb. 12 oz. She gained 7 oz. in a week! However, when I weighed her at the doctor's office a week and a half ago she had only gained 1 oz. in the five days we were home.

Yesterday Meredith turned six months old and we held a "welcoming and naming ceremony" at my parent's home in Cobden. We were joined by our immediate family and by the minister who married Tim and I in the same garden five years ago on June 19. The sun was shining when we gathered in the garden at 10 a.m. Nanny Keon made a gown for Meredith out of cotton incorporating my wedding veil into it. Tiny seashells picked on the beaches of the west coast dangled from cream satin ribbons. It was so beautiful and creative. It was such a special outfit for Meredith's important day. My sisters, Lana and Stephanie, sang songs including "I Hope You Dance." Tim's sister, Sherry, and his Aunt Diane said the readings. We planted an oak tree for Meredith and everyone took turns shovelling earth around the tree. Tim and I read a letter to Meredith as well. The ceremony was filled with love and joy and celebration.

After the ceremony we were treated to a gourmet brunch that my mom and sister Lana put together. It was refreshing to share this day with our family. We had originally planned to have a party after our birth, and when that couldn't happen we planned to do something after Meredith arrived home from the hospital. It seemed there was always something stopping us. How wonderful to plan this day and to have it work out. We couldn't have asked for a better day.

Meredith has been showing signs of teething in the past few weeks. She also seems to be trying to hold her head up on her own. Her neck muscles are getting stronger. She is having her eyesight tested on Wednesday, June 9.

So this week will bring more adventures, I am sure. I am determined to get answers, or at least to investigate what is going on with Meredith. I am tired of getting the run-around and we are certainly not going to "wait and see" any longer. Enough is enough. We have started to train a family relief worker so that we can get a few little breaks throughout the month as we need it. Lack of sleep makes everything a hundred times worse.

Sunday, June 27, 2004

Meredith had her eyes tested and structurally both eyes are perfectly normal! The doctor explained that we see with our brains not our eyes, so we will wait and see how well Meredith actually sees. He doesn't expect she'll need glasses. Meredith is doing well these days tracking and following things. When I walk through the room she'll turn her head and follow me until I am out of sight. She continues to use her neck muscles and is getting stronger. We know that one day soon she will master holding her head up on her own. We put her on her stomach for the first time a couple of days ago and she seemed quite content with this. She managed to hold her head up and look around for a good while. At one point she turned her head to lay it down on the bed and looked at Tim. He got up and left the room. Slowly but surely, she lifted her head and couldn't quite make the full turn and did a face plant instead!

Tim spent his first Father's Day weekend visiting family. Meredith's Grandpa Graham had a big birthday party on the Saturday and then we went to Cobden Sunday morning to see my dad.

Tim and I made a decision a few weeks ago to sell our home here in Carleton Place. Our house sold within three days of being listed and so we have a mere eight weeks to pack. It will be further away from Tim's work but closer to our families.

Unfortunately, Meredith and I are checking into Hotel CHEO tomorrow. Meredith continues to have problems with her gastro-intestinal tract and the extreme pain she endures resulting in screaming fits has put Tim and I over the deep end. It was excruciating to see her suffering and in obvious pain in the first week, but now after six weeks of this we are over-stressed. I would rather be tortured than have to spend any more time standing helplessly by watching Meredith in such pain. Finally, CHEO is admitting us, and blood work will be done to determine the cause. We obviously hope for something that is easily managed. We are hoping that we will only be at CHEO for a few days and that we will be let out for the long weekend, as Tim has four days off. The last place we want to be is in the hospital.

Monday, July 12, 2004

We are beginning our third week at Hotel CHEO. Meredith has had just about every test possible in an attempt to find out what could be upsetting her gastro-intestinal (GI) tract. She had a scope done of her stomach and bowel on Canada Day. It took place in the OR under general anesthetic. The GI specialist met with us afterwards to show us images of Meredith's pink and healthy looking belly and bowel, as well as the fundoplication, which, by the way, was intact. We have been told for months that the retching is neurological and that she will eventually grow out of it.

The doctor explained that when she got the scope down into Meredith's tummy she came upon the balloon that anchors the feeding tube in place. She was unable to get passed it on either side and had to remove water from it in order to bypass it to explore her bowel. This feeding tube had been causing an obstruction all along! I was, and still am, furious that Meredith had to suffer for so long and that her troubles were blamed on a neurological problem.

Can you imagine the trauma, pain and discomfort Meredith has endured on average eight to ten times a day due to an obstruction in her stomach/ top of bowel? I asked about that feeding tube as it seemed to be the source of her discomfort all along. In hindsight, everything seems to make sense.

After a review of scope images a surgeon (not ours) determined that Meredith was simply too small to handle a low profile feeding tube at this time. So it was removed and replaced with the ugly, brown tube that she had right after her surgery back in January. We had never been able to release gas from her stomach with venting while she had the feeding tube. Now we can, and realize the amount of pain this has caused Meredith.

Since the feeding tube was removed 10 days ago, Meredith's pain symptoms have virtually disappeared. My mind wanders sometimes to thoughts of what Meredith has had to endure then I stop these images in their tracks.

It is too much to bear. I told a friend who also has a child with special needs that to make it through these experiences one must shut down a part of their hearts and heads, like a survival mechanism. People ask me how we can leave Meredith at CHEO at night. It pains us, of course, to leave her there, but in order for us to remain healthy and continue her care we need to trust the people at CHEO to care for Meredith. As soon as I walk out of the hospital I stop thinking about it all. I must.

Unfortunately, we have another challenge to face. Meredith started having consistent and severe arching, which we hadn't seen before even though this is common in children with CP. It is tough to see her dealing with uncontrollable spasms and they seem to cause her anxiety. We cannot manage her like this. Tim and I just want to see her comfortable and out of pain regardless of what needs to be done. The EEG performed last week determined that all seizure activity has stopped in her brain and as a result her anti-seizure medication has been discontinued. Now she is on only one medication, which hopefully will help reduce, or even eliminate the arching. We keep our fingers crossed.

Meredith has been exerting so much energy from constant arching that she still hasn't gained weight. In order to help her gain weight without an unreasonable amount of expressed breast milk, we decided to add a formula concentrate to the breast milk to boost her caloric intake while maintaining a manageable volume.

So now we will wait to see how she manages with this new medication and the hospital wants to see some weight gain before they will discharge us. In the meantime, we bought a house in my hometown not far from my parents. We have to be out of the house we are in now in the next 10 days. Thankfully, we have help to get things packed up this week and then the move will take place a week from Saturday. We'll be living with my parents for the month of August while we do some cosmetic work to the new house. We are excited to begin anew.

The last two weeks have been extremely emotional for us. Most days I feel as though I am going to war as I answer the same questions over and over again. For the most part, the staff is excellent and Meredith has quite a few admirers and many empathetic nurses caring for her. I suppose I lack patience when it comes to things like medical students explaining to me that supplementation is required since Meredith isn't gaining weight on my breast milk. I inhale, breathe and then explain how the obstruction in her stomach resulted in her inability to gain weight. I am exhausted and depleted and ready to get home with Meredith.

Tim works each day and joins us at CHEO after work for a couple of hours. He feels just as helpless, but for another reason, he cannot be with us throughout the day. The nurses admire him for his gentle care, firm commitment and dedication to Meredith. Needless to say, life hasn't been easy lately but we are coping and managing to survive. Having a good sleep, a sense of humour and a lot of love in our lives seems to do the trick.

Saturday, July 17, 2004

For those of you who have endured any type of trauma in your life, you will understand that sometimes a bubbly sense of humour can take a turn and before you know it, you are the proud owner of a dark sense of humour. Some might argue that this is a coping mechanism and may be a veil for deep-seated denial. I would disagree. I believe that those who withstand the difficult and traumatic times in life are blessed with a sense of humour, possess some degree of hope and trust that all will be well at the end of the day. This may explain why some people thrive in the face of adversity, while others merely survive.

Though we don't particularly want to be at CHEO there are always lessons to be learned. I am often amazed by people who provide advice to me about raising a child with special needs when they have never had to walk in these shoes. In the beginning I was very defensive and insulted, but now I remind myself that people are often ignorant, sometimes insensitive, and most times simply trying to be helpful. I have learned that people will attempt to imagine themselves in our situation, and when they figure they would never be able to handle what we're going through, they assume that we must be in denial since we appear happy and adjusted. Tim and I have a choice–either to cry by Meredith's bedside, or to enjoy every single minute we have with her.

Perhaps the greatest challenge over the past few weeks at CHEO has been the bold assumptions that Tim and I are in denial. Numerous comments have been made to me about Meredith's birth and how perhaps, as an example, I might have been "too small" to accommodate a baby naturally. I am grateful that I had five busy years of experience as a doula before giving birth to Meredith. Ignorance around childbirth has always been a major hurdle for birth professionals. I worry for a mother who does not have my experience and might take these comments personally, and blame herself unnecessarily for the outcome of her birth. Telling me, or anyone else, that "perhaps things would have been different if you were in the hospital" or "maybe you should have had a C-section," does nothing to help or ease the burdens we face.

Meredith is surrounded by incredible nurses. They are disappointed when Tim arrives. They know the cuddles with her will stop! Today we slipped out for lunch and left Meredith with one of her primary nurses. When we returned, we found Meredith in her crib, fast asleep. There was a post-it note attached to her that said, "Don't wake our baby bear." Although it is extremely difficult to leave each evening, I know that Meredith will be tended to quickly should she awake. We know she isn't likely to be lying in her crib but is more likely to be found behind the nurses' station in someone's arms. CHEO has also provided a sitter to come and sit by Meredith's bedside from 7 p.m. until 7 a.m. each night. During the day, I often have our family relief worker come for a few hours so that I can get out, eat and take a breather. We will be sad to lose her when we move from Lanark County.

We will remain at CHEO for another week at least. Our medical student and the senior resident have both made Meredith their project. They both finish their work on our floor on Friday and they want Meredith hopefully discharged by then. She is responding well to the new medications and her arching has reduced significantly. It's now a matter of adjusting the dose to find a happy balance. The pain management specialist has been very compassionate. He suggests that Meredith needs time to unwind after being in such pain for so long. We feel relieved when we know she has slept well and is calmer and more content during the day. Our lives boil down to one thing, if Meredith is happy, we are happy. It is that simple.

My mom, sister Stephanie, and friend, Emmanuelle, arrived early Thursday morning and packed up 90 per cent of our house. What an enormous weight they lifted from our shoulders. Last night, we arrived home with Tim's dad and stepmother loading up a big trailer with boxes, and packing more items. Tim and his dad also moved most of the furniture. Our old house is bare and we are excited to get into our new house in the fall.

Finally, Meredith gained a whopping ounce on Friday and will be weighed again tomorrow. We hope to see more weight gain in the days to come.

Saturday, July 31, 2004

We were discharged on Friday, July 23, and drove straight to my parent's house from CHEO. The next morning, Tim and I, with help, returned to our old place to finish moving, and to clean the house for the new owners.

Meredith is doing well. At discharge she weighed an incredible 12 lb. 8 oz. I suspect she is now at least 13 pounds! She will be weighed on Wednesday when our new dietitian visits. We spent our first weekend in Cobden regrouping and helping Meredith to adjust to life outside CHEO. She usually has a fussy period after being there. Here we are a week later and Meredith is doing great.

Last Sunday, I got my first grin from Meredith. We see more hints of smiling from her. She is in such good humour when she awakes in the morning. She starts to kick her legs and gets very excited. It is such a joy! She is also focusing on our faces more and is interested in her mobile and anything shiny or metallic. She is heavier now and prefers to be in our arms. I wonder how the last few months have interfered with her development. She is on medication to help reduce the arching and to relax her muscles. The break from the arching is good for her. Today, Tim re-introduced the soother and she was quite interested.

Meredith and I now have a whole new team of caregivers to meet and get to know. Renfrew County has excellent services and we are eligible for 40 hours of nursing care per month and 60 hours per month of care from a personal support worker. This will be a huge improvement. It will be a relief to have people trained in caring for Meredith so that Tim and I can get out on our own sometimes. It brings so much comfort knowing that there is support when we hit the tough times. This week we will meet our new occupational therapist and will spend four hours with our personal support worker. We aim to have training out of the way before we move into our new house.

What a change for us to have our family around. When I need to express milk or grab a bite to eat, my dad is here during the day to entertain her. It is beneficial to have various people handling Meredith. She seemed to be "making strange" for our first couple of days here, but now is content in Nanny, Poppa and Aunt Stephanie's arms. Her Great Aunt Odel held her yesterday and she was very aware that a new person was holding her. She knows what is going on and who her mother and father are.

I am beginning to let go of the difficult days spent at CHEO and starting to relax a little. I still have anger about how some things were handled, but in time I will work through them. Mom assures me every day that I need never apologize for venting. I didn't like that the anger was beginning to eat away at me and that I was feeling cynical and negative when I awoke each day. I know how unhealthy unresolved feelings can be to the mind and body. I feel a shift has taken place and that my anger is beginning to dissolve. One of the best medicines is being "home," surrounded by love and perspective. Tim and I are beginning to turn our focus to the days and weeks ahead, talking about our new home and our future here in Cobden.

Wednesday, August 11, 2004

I wish I could write about how things have continued to improve but that is not the case. We had been seeing some episodes of retching but thought little of it. Things became worse rather quickly. Meredith is well otherwise but is retching frequently throughout the day. This is exactly what she went through when she was on the Nitrazepam, which resulted in hospitalization.

One of the medications she is taking right now is from the same family of drugs as the Nitrazepam. Before we assumed anything, we tinkered with the rate of her feeds, got rid of the formula concentrate for a couple of days, and even had an x-ray done to check the position of the tube. After ruling out all other possibilities we concluded that it is indeed the Clonazepam.

Thankfully, our neurologist agrees. We have started the slow process of weaning her off of it, or at the very least reducing the dose as a starting point. Meredith had at least been sleeping and resting well but in the last few days that is no longer the case. It is extremely frustrating, and once again we stand helplessly by as she struggles for comfort.

I weighed Meredith last Wednesday and she had gained 8 oz. in only 10 days bringing her weight up to 13 lb. We were thrilled! I had her weighed today and she has lost a whole ounce. Today Meredith had a vomiting episode at the community health centre about a block away from our home where I weigh her. I dropped to my knees, stuck the venting syringe in her G-tube and held a tissue under her chin. The force of the retching is so powerful that she will blow the adapter out of the end of the G-tube if we do not grab it immediately. This would result in all of her stomach contents being lost on the floor. I know, very graphic. Welcome to our reality. I think the nurse was somewhat horrified and immediately helped before taking us into a small room while

Meredith and I got our bearings. I thought it might be interesting to make a film and call it "A Day in the Life of Meredith."

On a happier note, Meredith is now able to turn on to her back when we place her on her stomach. She has great head control and pushes herself up with her arms and looks around. Our physiotherapist, infant development worker and occupational therapist are pleased that she is doing this on her own. She has also started "making strange" in the last month, which is a good sign as far as development goes. It makes it a bit hard on me though, as I cannot leave her with many people to get a break. Obviously she loves to be with Tim and is also happy resting on my mom in the evenings. We have so much support available to us, but it seems rather useless right now since handing her over to someone is stressful. I do have a personal support worker coming tomorrow for training so hopefully Meredith will cooperate.

Meredith will attend a seating clinic at the Renfrew office of the Ottawa Children's Treatment Centre in September to be fitted for a special needs stroller. It can take six or more months after ordering to receive it. We hope to have it for the spring of 2005. In the meantime, we may be able to get one on loan.

We are quickly getting exhausted these days and hope that this retching problem gets resolved soon. We feel that after eight months we all deserve a little break. We are told that it gets easier but some days I wonder if that will be the case for us. I think back to our early days when we first brought Meredith home from the hospital and shudder to think of how new everything was. We somehow managed to find our way to where we are now. Reflecting on where we have been and how far we have come helps me to see that it is getting easier.

Monday, August 23, 2004

Meredith had her appointments at CHEO. The new G-tube placement went well. Meredith wasn't in as much discomfort as she was the last time because I gave her some codeine beforehand. I promised her that I would never let her go through any procedure like that again without having some pain relief.

I remembered the last time she had a G-tube inserted. It was sheer agony for her, and that put me in tears before the procedure even got started this time. The anticipation was worse than the event itself. Meredith has lost more weight, five oz. in five days bringing her weight down to 12 lb. 10 oz. Our neurologist expressed concern. We have been tinkering with the dosages of her medications this week and yet the retching continues and the arching has worsened.

We decided today to put Meredith on continuous feedings. We'll do this for three days to see if things improve. There was a week and a half of peace between the time she had the low profile feeding tube removed and when the Clonazepam was started. There is more evidence that her stomach is emptying at a very slow pace. This probably has a lot to do with her discomfort, retching and the screaming fits that have started to appear again on and off. Our neurologist feels that the medications might be relaxing her digestive tract. We will see if our little experiment of continuous feedings will make a difference.

Meredith attended her first wedding this past weekend. My younger sister, Stephanie, and her new uncle, Robin, tied the knot at a beautiful morning ceremony followed by an outdoor dinner and live music to celebrate. Meredith was fairly overwhelmed by the noise so she spent the better part of the day inside with our new caregiver, Leslie.

Tim and I have started work on the new house. The kitchen floor is being installed tomorrow. We take ownership on Friday but are still not sure when we will move in. There is still a lot of work to be done before we can call it home. Thankfully, Mom and Dad will keep us for a couple of more weeks.

We are hoping things are sorted out soon for Meredith. Our hearts can't take much more of this. Living one day at a time is starting to get very old. It is time for more peace and joy in our lives.

Monday, September 6, 2004

I am writing from CHEO this cloudy morning. Tim has returned to Cobden to work on our new home while Meredith and I remain here. We celebrated Tim's birthday together on Saturday. We seem to be at CHEO for many holidays and special days throughout the year. It is our wish to be at home once Meredith's first birthday rolls around. Meredith was nine months old yesterday. I am amazed at how fast the time has passed.

We were admitted to CHEO on Wednesday, August 25. Meredith's retching went from bad to really bad. Our neurologist asked us to bring Meredith in by noon. We were warmly welcomed by the nurses on 4-East, which made returning a little easier. Meredith's feedings were immediately stopped and she was put on IV fluids for 24 hours. We were unable to have a milk study done before Tuesday, August 31, so we spent that first weekend just sitting around and waiting.

Tim had Friday and Monday off so he moved most of our things into the new house with the help of his dad and some family friends. In the 12 days since Meredith and I arrived here, new flooring has been installed in the kitchen and upstairs bathroom, all carpets have been removed, and all of the wallpaper has been stripped. The kitchen and laundry room have been completely redone and painting will begin soon. Our parents have been working cleaning, laying floors, hauling carpet out and generally preparing things for decorating.

Back to our CHEO experience…The milk study showed that Meredith's tummy is emptying VERY slowly. Her feedings were started again with expressed breast milk. Gradually the rate has increased and we are almost at the full volume Meredith requires. She has started on yet another medication to help with her stomach's motility and it seems to be working well. She weighed in at 12 lb. 6.5 oz. on September 4, and when weighed this morning, only two days later, she weighed 12 lb. 13 oz.

On Thursday, September 2, I discovered that Meredith had a pretty serious urinary tract infection. Antibiotics were started Friday night and by Sunday, Meredith seemed less irritable and had stopped arching. These symptoms are likely to have been triggered by the UTI. This morning Meredith is even better than yesterday, although not fully back to her old self just yet.

We discovered a while ago that Meredith is attracted to shiny things so shortly after we arrived last week, I went down to the gift shop to purchase a mylar, metallic balloon. When she awoke from her nap, I showed it to her. I was blessed with the biggest, toothless smile I had ever seen on Meredith's face. Oh, the joy in her eyes! You would know she was smiling just by her eyes. I thought it might have been a one-time experience but it has been ongoing. Tim and I even got some smiles when she looked at us upon waking and recently she has started to smile at herself in the mirror. The severe arching has interfered somewhat, but we are hoping that once the UTI is cleared up the arching will lessen. Seeing her smile and being recognized when she looks at us has been an enormous milestone and highlight of the last nine months. That balloon was the best five dollars I have ever spent.

Monday, September 13, 2004

We have received our probation papers! We were waiting for Meredith's feeding scheduled to become more regular and thought ourselves quite capable of managing at home. The senior resident agreed and said we could leave. We arrived back in Cobden by late afternoon on Sunday.

Meredith was nine months old on September 5, and coincidently there has been a shift in my thinking and in the way I feel. Coming to CHEO has never been a joyful experience. I dreaded coming here and leaving Meredith at night. I hated our lives being bombarded with questions, comments and unsolicited advice. Our previous visit was very stressful for me. So much happened that it took time for me to recover.

This time though, I felt strong, and the self-doubt that always seemed to have accompanied my strong intuitive feelings has subsided. Perhaps because of "sticking to my guns" and not being intimidated, or so blindly trusting what the "experts" had to say. I leave here this time feeling stronger, more empowered and very confident.

As each crisis occurs one must take time to withdraw and consider. If we allow ourselves to face situations head-on, they transform into something new, something we are able to accept and to rise above. I wonder about the woman I was before Meredith was born. I remember "her" and yet, "she" seems so far away. I trust that this is a normal part of becoming a mother for the first time.

With that said, the CHEO experience, for me, isn't what it used to be. We know that our nurses on 4-East know Meredith well enough that we don't worry when we are not with her. I know she will be well loved and in good hands. Being told that, and feeling that as a mother are two very different things. There will be many more trips to CHEO but I won't dread them as much. Although I know that trips back to CHEO are inevitable it won't be so horrible now.

The plan now is to finish the house, get unpacked and settle into our new abode. I am excited to see all the work that has been done since I've been away and to take part in the painting and renovating.

Saturday, October 2, 2004

As summer turns to autumn, Tim and I are like a pair of squirrels preparing our home for the winter. Of course we're not doing it alone. We have had tremendous help from our families and from members in our community.

On the day I last wrote (September 13), Meredith started retching again. Tim and I were discouraged once again. Then we made the connection that it was four days after she started on the formula concentrate again. The same thing happened the last time we were discharged from CHEO. We decided to discontinue the formula concentrate to see if things improved. Meredith's volume of breast milk had to increase in order for her to get the extra calories. This meant I had to start expressing again every three hours around the clock. Suddenly I felt as though I had been launched into those first few weeks postpartum. Fortunately my body responded well and I was soon producing more milk. I was literally expressing for each feeding with no back-up supply. We were in crisis mode again.

While this was going on, Meredith improved and gained a whopping 5 oz. in only four and a half days. She wasn't even getting the volume of milk that she was "supposed" to get. I figured that we could try her on a lesser volume of milk to see if she gained weight. Why follow standard growth charts when we are not standard? I was researching alternatives for some kind of back-up should I suddenly be unable to express milk for Meredith, and for the future when Meredith transitions to formula. It is not practical to express milk for the next 15 years. I found a woman whose third child had similar feeding issues. She is sending me some samples of an organic formula that she used. She managed to give her child breast milk for three years with formula supplementation.

Last weekend, we tried Meredith on another type of formula as I am going to be away for one of her feedings. She seemed to tolerate it, and so we continued to add diluted concentrate to her feedings in order to build up a backup supply and for me to have a couple of pump-free nights. Sure enough, things got worse, and by Tuesday night Meredith was retching throughout the night. We made the decision once again to stop the formula and to return exclusively to breast milk.

We have discovered that all of the adjustments combined have made little difference. Whatever we're dealing with is aggravated by formula, rates of feeding, volume and positioning. Meredith is having a rough time and the last two nights have been hell. It has been 10 months since her birth and to be honest, things haven't become much easier. We've just become used to it. We are really no further ahead than we were in March.

Meredith has improved so much developmentally, but physically we continue to fight the same demon. I have felt for a long time now that there is something serious going on. Each visit to CHEO we find a possible cause of the retching and vomiting. Last time Meredith was put on medication to assist with the motility of her stomach. Although it helped a little it felt like a Band-Aid solution to whatever the problem really is, and that we would be returning again. Our wish was to have Meredith home for at least three months. It's only been three weeks and things are progressively getting worse. Perhaps it's time to go to Toronto for another opinion. Somebody, somewhere has seen this before, I am sure.

It doesn't make sense to return to CHEO. If her weight loss becomes significant then we will have to. At the time of our last discharge from CHEO, Meredith weighed 12 lb. 15 oz. After losing and gaining an ounce here and there over the last three weeks, Meredith now weighs 12 lb. 13 oz. We just can't seem to break that 13-pound mark.

Our house is transforming into a home, slowly but surely. With Tim commuting back and forth to Ottawa, Meredith's care, a CHEO stint, and sleep deprivation, we are not where we had hoped to be at this point as far as the house is concerned. The plan is to move into the house in the next couple of weeks though. We are so excited. This house is incredible and we look forward to a new chapter in our lives.

We continue to get lots of smiles from Meredith. She was very engaged until the last couple of days. She seemed to understand the whole concept of "peek-a-boo" and we could get her smiling with just a glance. These joyful moments will return again when she feels better. We are learning that she has some sensory sensitivity. If you sing to her she may look away periodically. It's difficult for her to process the sight of your face and the sound of your voice at the same time.

There are exercises to help with this but they are very specific and must be done for two weeks, every hour and a half while she is awake. We have decided to wait until we are settled in our new home before embarking on these exercises. The sensory difficulties might explain the severe reaction Meredith has when travelling in the car seat. We can't go anywhere now and only use the car for necessary appointments in Ottawa, and even then, sedation is necessary.

Our family relief worker is working out beautifully. I am so glad we have this in place, especially now that Tim and I are so sleep-deprived. It's comforting to know that there is someone else, other than us, to feed Meredith, administer her medications and care for her in a loving manner.

Sunday, October 10, 2004 CANADIAN THANKSGIVING WEEKEND
This Thanksgiving arrived with mixed emotions. I reflected on where I was a year ago. How very pregnant I was. My parents were in the process of building an addition to their house and we sat within the framed walls under the stars singing songs until well into the night. I belly danced with my sisters and felt so full of life. We were so very grateful for the blessings we had with our family, good health and careers and, of course, for the child who would be born within the coming months.

I have so much to be thankful for. The past 10 months have flown by–it hasn't been easy. Tim and I have been tested in so many ways and we feel thankful for our resilience and for the love we share that has held us together even in our darkest moments.

We are, of course, most thankful for the wee life that joined our family on December 5, 2003. Meredith has brought with her lessons that we would never have learned otherwise. We are thankful for our families and for our friends, and to strangers who have offered support. Some have contributed financially, some have made meals and some have donated their time to help us with daily tasks while Meredith was hospitalized. There has been generosity helping us move and prepare our new home. We received many cards and messages along the way. We will always be grateful. Without the uplifting words and kind gestures from so many people we would never have made it this far.

Not a day goes by that we do not celebrate Meredith's life and her presence here with us. We are acutely aware that we could have lost her in those first few hours. In the last three weeks I've attended the funerals of two babies, both born within a month of Meredith and both having arrived in this world with their own unique challenges.

Janna was born almost a month to the day after Meredith. We spent many days with her and her family on 4-East at CHEO. Janna was Meredith's first friend. Although they never actually met, her mother and I would talk to the babies giving updates of their friend's well-being. Janna passed away on September 22, in the arms of her parents.

A week later, we were devastated to learn that another wee soul, Thomas, passed away suddenly, also at CHEO. Thomas spent a couple of nights on 4-East while we were on an extended stay. I went to school with his parents so we always enjoyed a visit when I ran into them there. His mom and I planned to get together for tea with our babies once we were discharged from CHEO last time. Unfortunately, we never had the chance.

I think of these two babies every single day and hold Meredith a little closer. There are never guarantees in life. I have pondered many things and wondered what the purpose of it all is. Perhaps this is where faith comes in. I have to admit, faith can sometimes get lost in the chaos of our reality. In the quiet moments, I find myself coming back to that part of me that firmly believes that there is a purpose to everything even when it is so difficult to understand.

Saturday, October 23, 2004

Today was our official moving day. Tim and his parents, with help from my dad and my sister, Lana, moved everything from the storage unit to the new house. We discovered after buying the house that there were no heating vents upstairs. We will get our heating system updated and renovated in November and decided to move in anyway, hopefully by next weekend. We will use a space heater in our bedroom until the heat vents are installed. We have missed having a space of our own and our independence. Living with my parents and having their constant support has been a godsend, but we're ready to be on our own again and enjoy our new house.

We tried a simple experiment after the Thanksgiving weekend and Meredith has improved significantly. Fortunately, our occupational therapist is obsessed with feeding issues and after attending several workshops she suggested that perhaps Meredith is still refluxing. Maybe not refluxing the milk, but perhaps refluxing the gases produced in her stomach, as well as stomach acid.

She told us of a neuroscientist who suggests that although the milk studies might show that there isn't any active refluxing, there could be refluxing of the acidic stomach gases. The esophagus starts producing copious amounts of mucous to protect itself and to protect the lungs. The vicious cycle of choking on the mucous can apparently trigger a cough and retching followed by vomiting. It can also result in severe arching, triggering coughing, which in turn triggers retching, and the cycle begins again. The more the feedings are increased, the more stomach acid is produced and therefore more refluxing. Although the different formulas and rates of feedings made a difference temporarily, they were all just Band-Aid solutions.

We know she does better on breast milk only. It is easily digestible and leaves her stomach more quickly with less reflux aggravation. This doctor also says that since so many of the symptoms of this mimic neurological behaviours, like arching, that infants and children with neurological impairment are often heavily medicated to combat these behaviours when in fact the child is only demonstrating the symptoms of excruciating pain. She suggested we start weaning Meredith off her medications. We consulted her doctors at CHEO and they agreed that they haven't been able to offer any other options, so figured it was worth a try.

The most incredible solution to our problem though has been daily doses of regular, over-the-counter liquid antacid! It acts as a barrier between the stomach and the esophagus. We saw a difference within 24 hours. It is unbelievable.

Meredith still has some retching but less than half of what she was experiencing before the antacid. Finally she has gained weight and as of October 12, she weighed 13 lb. We are gradually weaning her off of the Clonazepam and have reduced the Tizanidine from three doses to one per day. If we notice increased arching we will refrain from any further decrease of the Clonazepam. The neuroscientist says that the Clonazepam actually aggravates the problem. Although we're not 100 per cent better, we are much better than we were.

After a full week of reduced retching, we were shocked to discover that Meredith hadn't gained even an ounce of weight. I couldn't believe my eyes. I dropped my head and started to cry. And then I couldn't stop. I cried while I dressed her. I cried all the way home and then I cried some more when I got home. I cried for all of the times we have wracked our brains trying to figure out what the problem might be. I cried for the fact that once again, no matter how hard we try, our hopes are crushed. I cried for Meredith as she has no choice but to endure the pain each day brings. I cried for all of the battles I have had with "professionals" about the importance of continuing to give Meredith breast milk. I cried and cried and cried. Then I took a deep breath and gathered my senses and carried on.

We have increased her caloric intake and after almost three days, Meredith gained an ounce. We are again hopeful that there will be further weight gain by Tuesday when she is weighed again.

Meredith cut two bottom teeth this past week, an adventure of its own. Two little teeth can sure cause a lot of problems in a little body. Her G-tube site started leaking out of nowhere, and when I called CHEO, I was told that this is a common problem when infants with G-tubes begin teething. It has something to do with an increase of gastric juices produced. After a rough week all around Meredith has two shiny, little teeth. There are more to come and we're not looking forward to it, but at least we know what to expect.

Sunday, December 5, 2004

I just glanced at the clock and it reads "7:23 p.m." And so here we are, one year later…Today, we celebrated Meredith's first year of life. Love filled our home today. Each person present on that night a year ago was here with us. We were surrounded by our incredible families who have been with us every step of this journey. Two of our nurses from CHEO made the trek from Ottawa to be with us, and our former infant development worker from Carleton Place joined us too. Representatives from everyone who have shared this journey from day one were here. There was laughter, reflection and joy. Tim and I agreed that we both felt tremendous relief having made it to this day. It has been a hard road and we are better people because of it. Meredith was content and didn't seem to mind the attention she received all day. We had a cake with a rainbow on it that said, "You've come a long way, baby. Happy 1st Birthday!" Meredith even had a taste of the frosting. She received this beautiful letter from my sister, Stephanie:

> "…The seasons have rolled around once more, to bring us another cold December day. Yet, how different are our celebrations this year! On your birthday, your friends and family have gathered around you to surround you with love and to infuse you with the power that comes with being in a gentle community. When I see you smile at your mom and dad and the proud smiles that result from it, I think back to another December when it seemed that all the doctors could do was set limits on you. Now, your smile inspires many others! Now, you look to the door when it opens to see who your latest visitor is.

You have overcome tremendous challenges in this past year. You have learned so much! In spite of the obstacles you face and the pain you endure, you now manage to express your joy when you see your mommy and daddy's faces, and your dismay when either of them leaves the room.

Beloved, little precious one, the sky is the limit! We all have faith in you! We triumph with you when you learn something new. We love and believe in you. Thank you for enriching us all, and for fighting to stay alive on that December night that now seems so long ago. Celebrating here with you is a dream come true for all of us."

As always, your loving aunt,
Stephanie

Monday, December 6, 2004

It is 5:57 a.m. Meredith and I awoke about an hour ago shortly after Tim started getting ready for work.

It is obvious that a gathering took place here yesterday. I came downstairs, sat on the couch and felt enormous peace, relief and a sense of accomplishment. We made it through the first year! I cannot count the number of times nurses, doctors, social workers and other caregivers told us that we just needed to make it through the first year, that it would be the toughest. I hung on to those words as though my very life depended on it, saying them to myself like a mantra…"Just get through this first year."

I didn't expect to experience the intense feelings of relief when this milestone was reached. Working on what I refer to now as Meredith's Life Albums has been a form of therapy for me. Yesterday, everyone took turns reading through the three books I had created, and looking at the photos illustrating a life that has endured and overcome tremendous obstacles. My mom said that going through the albums was like experiencing this whole journey again, obviously to a lesser degree. The first half of the first album, from conception to the end of pregnancy, is filled with anticipation, excitement and an underlying feeling of innocence. After Meredith's birth there is a sense of shock that turns to deep sadness and heaviness. This gradually turns to hope, and when volume two begins there is a sense of joy as the initial CHEO experience comes to an end and we begin life anew at home. Each page stirs up more feelings of joy, hope and acceptance. By the end of volume three, you feel as though you have arrived to a good place and from here on in, nothing will be insurmountable.

For many of us, Meredith's first birthday brought a feeling of closure especially for those who were there at the moment she arrived and witnessed that traumatic moment firsthand. One of our midwives hadn't seen Meredith since that first week. It must have been gratifying and healing for her to see us yesterday celebrating, laughing and perfectly accustomed to what has become our "normal."

Everything changed at 7:23 p.m. on December 5, 2003. Tim and I have walked a very scary road together and sometimes apart. We find ourselves now looking at all we have experienced, laughing in the face of adversity and at life itself. We know that our love for one another has reached levels that wouldn't have been possible had Meredith not been born.

Afterword

That is how it all began. My original online journal was written for those who desperately wanted to support us. I wanted to keep them in the loop about what was happening on a regular basis. Living in the NICU separated us from our families, friends and support network and so this diary served as a lifeline not only for them, but also for us. We would arrive home each evening, battered and worn from another long and hectic day in the hospital, to messages of hope and words of encouragement. I will always remember each one who took the time to write. They'll never know how valuable their words were to us at such a challenging time.

It never occurred to us that we would become parents of a medically fragile baby because we did everything right from the beginning to ensure a positive outcome. Those early hours, days and weeks were devastating, shocking and life-changing. The only way we could manage each day was to put every bit of our energy into living in the moment. Anything outside of that moment proved unbearable.

Becoming Meredith's mother 14 years ago has challenged me on every level–physically, mentally, emotionally and spiritually. Since the age of 13, I've watched Oprah's TV talk show and wondered when my big life challenge would present itself. I watched the countless stories of regular, everyday people being called to their own challenging journeys. My journey began the moment I learned that Meredith's life was going to take a different path than anticipated. Although I had a vague sense that one does not get through life without facing at least one gigantic, life-altering experience, I wasn't ready for it. It knocked me to my core. My initial response was, "You got the wrong person. I can't do this. I'm not strong enough."

On some level I knew this child was going to need an exceptional mother and I did not believe I could fill that role. Any of you who have walked the early days of a diagnosis knows that anxiety can creep up and grab hold of you at any given moment, especially as you learn more about what you and your loved one may potentially be dealt. I felt oddly privileged at times to mother this exceptionally fragile baby and at other times I literally threw my fists towards the sky as if to yell, "Is this all you've got?"

If you have found yourself on this path, you will inevitably learn lessons. You have to be willing to grow and evolve. You can just as easily choose to be bitter about what life hands you and spend the rest of your days miserable, angry and resentful.

All of us who are privileged to have been born and to live have choices to make. We will decide how we will move forward regardless of what life hands us. Although Meredith will not experience life as we had imagined and hoped she would, she is a human being who exudes love and joy despite her limitations and her pain. Her presence in our lives has not only taught my husband Tim and me the greatest of life lessons, but also everyone who has spent time with her.

We have managed to rise above our difficulties, with gratitude, hope and, most of all, pure love for the little soul who came to us on a cold December night in 2003. In the beginning we were under the mistaken belief that Meredith depended on us to lead the way. Over time we have learned that Meredith was leading the way. All we had to do was follow her lead, trusting that she wouldn't lead us astray.

What I Would Tell You - *The Original Essay*

I sensed someone watching as I comforted my daughter after a particularly traumatizing dental appointment at the Children's Hospital. I looked up and saw you staring at us from across the waiting room. I didn't pay much attention, as I have grown accustomed to the curious eyes of onlookers. Our daughter was born on December 5, 2003. After an abrupt lack of oxygen at birth she changed the course of our lives forever. Perhaps our lives unfolded exactly as they were meant to–they just didn't unfold in the way we had imagined or planned.

I talked to my daughter, kissed her and hugged her. I was giving her a brief break before putting her through the next traumatic experience of the day – the car ride home. Having cerebral palsy is the least of her worries, but this condition can turn a car seat into a torture chamber.

I stood up to gather our things, my daughter in my arms, and it was then that I noticed you were holding an infant. It was difficult to know for certain how old she was. I knew immediately though, that you were one of us. I knew that only recently your life had drastically changed and you sat here in this Children's Hospital wondering, "How did we get here?" I should have recognized that shocked stare because I once had it too. And I assume that the man sitting next to you, looking equally tired and shocked was your husband.

I made my way toward the doors and as I passed, our eyes met and I smiled at you. You smiled back and for a moment I knew that you knew, that I understood.

If I could, I would tell you that although you might not believe it right now, you will be okay. I would tell you to dig deep within yourself because you will find the strength and resilience somehow and it will surprise you. I would tell you to honour your feelings and let the tears flow when they need to. You will need the energy for more important things than holding in your emotions.

I would tell you that the man sitting next to you might cope differently and he might even want to run the other way. But I would tell you to hang on because he is scared and he really doesn't want to leave you. I would tell you to look after yourself so that you can care for your child. Don't underestimate the power of good nutrition, exercise, sleep, supplements and an empathetic therapist.

234

I would tell you that grief will come and confuse you, because how can something that brings such joy also bring such sadness? I would tell you to let people into your lives to help you. Our children require a village to raise them. Access all of the services and resources available. Find someone who can learn how to care for your child so that you can have breaks and so you and your partner can go on dates, even small ones like a 20-minute stroll outside holding hands, sharing wine on the deck or even catching a movie.

I would tell you that you know your child best of all and that no matter what you are told by doctors and other professionals who will become a part of your life, YOU know the answers. You will teach them about your child. At times you will question the validity of your intuition but after a while you will become profoundly aware of how accurate your gut feelings are when it comes to your child.

I would tell you not to be a martyr. Caring for your child will require tremendous focus and unimaginable energy and it can burn you out and make you sick when you least expect it. I would tell you to let your guard down along the way so that you can stay healthy in your mind and spirit.

I would tell you to seek out mothers like yourself. This is indeed the road less travelled and you will feel alone along the way especially in the company of healthy children and their parents. Yes, you will feel isolated but know that we are here. Sometimes you have to look a little harder but we are here. You can find us online, in support groups and wandering the halls of the children's hospital.

I would tell you that you will know far too much about the human anatomy, neurology, gastroenterology, feeding tubes, and pharmaceuticals than a mother should ever have to know. I would also tell you to research and inform yourself but be careful not to become overwhelmed by all of the information available to you. Having some trust in what your child's specialists tell you can be very grounding. Other parents of children like ours can be a wealth of information.

I would tell you that this is not an easy life. It is tough–there is no doubt about it, but you are capable and the rewards are great. You may never see your child graduate from university, walk down the aisle or give birth to grandchildren but you will feel pure joy when your child laughs for the first time. You will celebrate the moment you connect with your non-verbal child. You will call your spouse at work to share that your child has gained weight because weight gain is a struggle with our children.

I would tell you that you will have to witness procedures and surgeries and suffering well beyond what any parent should ever have to bear. But I would tell you that you will be courageous and comforting because your child will experience far more suffering than any child should ever have to endure.

I would tell you that your life will not resemble the life you had planned. It will be as though you landed in Holland instead of Italy, but after some time you will adjust the dreams you had and this reality will be normal for you. You will dream new dreams.

I would tell you that you might find yourself staring death in the face during close calls. You will be asked to fill out "do not resuscitate" forms and although you might decide not to resuscitate in the event of a cardiac arrest, when the moment arises, you will panic to think that it could all come to an end. And I would tell you to not feel guilty in the darkest moments when you pray to God to take your child if it would mean the suffering would end. This might horrify you but know that your love for your child is so great that at times you will believe that death would be a blessing.

I would tell you that others will not understand. They can't. This is a unique and complex journey on all levels. We cannot expect anyone to get it. And I would tell you that people–the cashier at the grocery store or your insurance broker or even your hair stylist–will say inconsiderate things like, "God only gives these special kids to special mothers" and "God will only give you what you can handle." You will nod and smile but eventually you will look them right in the face and tell them that those simple maxims are bullshit.

I would tell you that imagining your future will be bittersweet and may involve a plan A and a plan B. Plan A will be what you will do if your child outlives the predicted life expectancy set forth by the experts and plan B will come into play if they do not. You will catch yourself casually discussing your future with the code phrases of plan A and plan B.

I would tell you that grief will creep up on you after years have passed and you least expect it, like at a wedding when the father and bride have their first dance or when you hear a birth announcement. It will also creep up on you when you see yourself in a new mother who is just beginning this journey.

I would tell you that you will recognize her because she is you, from many years ago. You will want to run to her and hug her and tell her that everything will be okay. You will want to save her from the pain and the hardship and the unknown.

But I would tell you that when you find yourself sitting at the children's hospital and you see a new mom and dad who are just starting this journey, you will smile at them and walk by as they have their own path to travel and it will be different from yours. It may be longer or shorter. It may be more or less complicated.

I would tell you that her searching eyes are looking for some sign that she will survive this. And you, smiling as you pass, with your child arching over your shoulder, will let her know that yes, she will survive this, and may even thrive.

Julie Keon's professional career began in the early 90s in the field of social work. She always had a strong desire to work with people as they navigated through life and its various challenges. Eventually, certifying as a birth and postpartum doula (DONA International), Julie founded Mother Nurture Childbirth Services in 1998, assisting couples through the childbirth experience and the early weeks at home with a new baby. Seeing the need for specific support, she created a workshop for women who had experienced difficult or traumatic births. In the fall of 2015, Julie retired from all birth related work.

She welcomed the opportunity to become a licensed marriage officiant for the province of Ontario in 2012. To expand her services, Julie graduated as a certified Life-Cycle Celebrant® in early 2013 from the Celebrant Foundation & Institute with a focus on funeral and end-of-life celebrations. She specializes in the creation and implementation of ceremonies to mark life's transitions from the start of life to the end of life and everything in between.

The first edition of her book *What I Would Tell You* suffered an unexpected hypoxic event of its own soon after its launch in May 2015. As a result, Julie created this revised and expanded edition in order to continue to make the book available to readers.

A graduate (April 2016) of the Beyond Yonder Virtual School for Community Deathcaring in Canada, Julie aims to educate and support her community in the reclamation of family-centred death care. In 2017, she created a unique, end-of-life preparation course (Ready or Not~ Preparing for the Inevitable) for members of the community.

Her interests include psychology, health, travel, cooking, writing, and staying vibrant and resilient while holding on to a sense of humour. She shares her life in the Ottawa Valley with her husband, Tim, and their daughter, Meredith.